NURSE MANAGERS' BOOKSHELF
A Quarterly Series
VOLUME 2, NUMBER 3, SEPTEMBER 1990

Management Styles and Corporate Culture

EDITORIAL ADVISORY BOARD

NURSE MANAGERS' BOOKSHELF
A Quarterly Series
VOLUME 2, NUMBER 3, SEPTEMBER 1990

Management Styles and Corporate Culture

G. RUMAY ALEXANDER, RN, EdD
Vice President for Clinical Affairs
Nursing Programs
Tennessee Hospital Association
Nashville, Tennessee

WILLIAMS & WILKINS
BALTIMORE · HONG KONG · LONDON · MUNICH
SAN FRANCISCO · SYDNEY · TOKYO

Editor: Susan M. Glover
Associate Editor: Marjorie Kidd Keating
Copy Editor: Linda Hansford
Designer: Norman W. Och/Wilma Rosenberger
Illustration Planner: Lorraine Wrzosek
Production Coordinator: Raymond E. Reter

Printed in the United States of America

ISBN 0-683-06535-1

90 91 92 93 94
1 2 3 4 5 6 7 8 9 10

MANAGING EDITOR'S FOREWORD

As we enter the last decade of the twentieth century, several of the trends predicted by author John Naisbitt in his best-seller, *Megatrends*, are emerging. How are these trends affecting health care delivery systems and health care providers? And, more importantly, how can we facilitate our staff's adjustment to, acceptance of, and comfort with these changes, which are sometimes exciting but more often disconcerting, if not downright anxiety provoking? In this second volume of *Nurse Managers' Bookshelf* we provide some answers to these questions, answers that will assist you with the toughest—and most important—part of your job, the PEOPLE PART.

As nursing departments become decentralized, head nurses are undergoing role changes. Your old role as a boss is giving way to a new role as a coach or advisor; you are deriving more credibility from your managerial expertise than from your clinical competence; you are developing management techniques that encourage employee risk taking and innovative problem solving; and you are giving people the trust that they deserve. Without abdicating your responsibilities as a manager, you have been building relationships and putting issues in proper perspective, recognizing that unpopular decisions are sometimes part of the job.

Recognizing your need to stay informed about emerging issues as well as the potential for enhancing your value to the organization with a global perspective, the Editorial Advisory Board has chosen ethics, information systems, managerial styles, and problem employee behaviors as topics for this year's volume. These four issues will provide a fresh perspective, stimulate thinking, and cultivate self-esteem as the keys to employee satisfaction and empowerment, with resulting quality patient care. As always, we would like to hear your thoughts and reactions to these topics and your suggestions for future issues.

Susan M. Glover, RN, MSN
Managing Editor

PREFACE

I once heard a speaker say that the key to walking on water is knowing where the stones are. That is what I have tried to do in this issue—identify the stones.

You don't have to like everyone you meet or every situation you encounter. It is imperative that you strive to understand people, agendas, group dynamics, and how to make things work for you.

Human engineering is a daily challenge because it is predictably unpredictable. No one book can equip you fully. Some of your learning can only be gained through experience. However, you can benefit from the lessons and insights of others. I hope that, through this book, I can get you off to a wonderful start.

May the force be with you!

G. Rumay Alexander, RN EdD

I have just a minute,

only sixty seconds in it.

Forced upon me,

can't refuse it,

didn't seek it,

didn't choose it,

I must suffer if I lose it.

Give account if I abuse it.

Just a tiny little minute,

but . . . eternity is in it.

The War Cry
Salvation Army
December 1989

CONTENTS

1

Value Systems

Individuals approach the world with their own perceptions of reality. Since each of us is unique, our perceptions of reality will vary greatly, as will our values and value judgments. Individuals choose, both consciously and unconsciously, what they hold as precious and dear and what is important to their core existence.

Thus individuals may share common events, but will view the experiences differently because their beliefs and values are different. A culture is basically a series of belief systems that have been strung together by our socio-cultural-ethnic backgrounds (Spector, 1979). A great deal of what we value is based on how these systems have been programmed (yes, we have been programmed) into the brain. The brain has been likened to a computer; it records everything. Who is the programmer? Our parents, the time in history in which we were born, and the events that we have experienced. The brain is information-addicted and thus thrives on input—much like Johnny 5 in the movie *Short Circuit*. Repeated patterns experienced by an individual over time are developed into circuits, or what we call habits. They are called up by various stimuli, often subconsciously. Thus, no one acts freely. The anatomical seat of one's habits is believed to lie in the reticular systems of the brain, located at the top of the brainstem. This area stores all habits and preferences, and there too lies one's value system. The Nobel Prize–winning neuroscientist Roger Sperry holds the view that the "mind" emerges when brain or nerve cells are organized in certain ways or in a pattern. We are born with a brain that is ready to be actively engaged by chemicals and other stimuli, and thus its development is beyond our control. The mind is another thing entirely; it is developed by the individual and can be changed by the individual by changing or rearranging patterns (circuits) of thinking (Rorick, 1984).

If you understand how individuals' value systems are influenced, you also can see how two people born at different times in history, but practicing the same profession with the same code of ethics and standards, bring to a situation different value systems. In today's work world there are basically three value sets in operation, based on time: "Pre–World War II," "TV Babies," and "Computer Babies" (Table 1.1).

Differences in mindset and their usages often result in perceptions that are at opposite ends of the spectrum, and this can fuel many stressful moments for managers. In most conflicts, there is a clash between the manager's and the subordinate's belief systems. Recognizing these various perspectives and being sensitive to them is important to being a good manager of people, and is one way to relieve stress.

Table 1.1.
Value Systems Based on Time

	"Pre–World War II"	"TV Babies"	"Computer Babies"
Values	Power hierarchy; work one's way up the ladder	Quality circles, participatory management, team building	Autonomy; like to work alone (Lone Ranger), desire little supervision
Goals	Get the job done out of pride, as a goal for the company and country	Personal growth; meaningful experience from doing the job	Get the job done so that leisure time can be used more satisfactorily
Work medium	Assembly line; human labor	Mainframe computer	Personal desktop computer
Time values	9–5; overtime	9–5; flexitime begins	Flexitime, flexiplace
Consumption	Brand-name buying; few choices available, few demanded	More choices available	More choices demanded

The field of value analysis can be very useful to managers as they attempt to understand individuals whose values differ from theirs. Some of the most noteworthy work was done by Dr. Clare W. Graves (cited in Mali, 1981), who identified seven different value systems. The first system mostly applies to infants and to those who may have mental impairments rendering them unable to work. The other six exist in most organizations, and for the sake of understanding both sides of the employment picture, these six systems are briefly described below.

System 2: Tribalistic

Employee	Supervisor
Desires to be told what to do	Monitors work closely
Money is important	Keeps his or her fingers in the work
Having a steady job is the focus	
Wants job expectations in detail	Delegates very little

System 3: Egocentric

Employee	Supervisor
Desires work freedom	Often described as tough
Money is important	Makes decisions for subordinates
Loves status symbols	
Wants outline of job expectations	Loyal to him- or herself

System 4: Conformist

Employee	Supervisor
Knows the rule book and follows it to the letter	Treats everybody the same
Money is important	Sees his or her role as the enforcer
Feels deep loyalty to the organization	Is "all business"

System 5: Manipulative

Employee	Supervisor
Wants to be left alone to do the job	Is very competitive
Money is important	Takes calculated risks
Has great need to be successful	Generally manages by objectives or exception

System 6: Sociocentric

Employee	Supervisor
Being liked is valued	Being liked is valued
Materialistic rewards are not top priority	Avoids disciplining others—distasteful
Has great need to socialize at all levels	Treats everybody the same

System 7: Existential

Employee	Supervisor
Likes to select his or her jobs	Sees him- or herself as resource person
Freedom is valued more than money	Leaves the "how to" up to the employee
Personal goals are top priority	Provides minimum supervision

Understanding the value systems of your employees should dictate your leadership style. You can work with those whose value systems are different from yours without passing judgment (Table 1.2).

Don E. Beck, director of the National Values Center in Denton, Texas, gave a talk in 1981 entitled, "Value Systems Reflect Natural Differences but They Can be Bridged." He shared a new system based on a psychological progression with seven separate stations or value system levels of psychological "coping."

Level 1: Survivalist view. It emphasizes survival, a fight against the elements.

Level 2: Tribalistic view. The world is mysterious, with both good and evil spirits at work.

Level 3: Pragmatic, aggressive view. The individual seeks personal gain regardless of damage to others.

Level 4: Newtonian view. The individual follows rules to maintain an orderly existence.

Level 5: Cornucopia view. The world has plenty of resources just waiting to be tapped by all.

Level 6: Philosophical view. The individual seeks to find peace in the inner self and in the inner self of others.

Level 7: Ecological demise view. The world is on the verge of collapse because humans have misused the natural resources available (Beck, 1981).

According to Beck, everyone falls into one of these viewpoints, and one cannot skip levels. The idea as a manager is to identify the levels of the participants and build a bridge between the two viewpoints. Beck calls it "finding a way to give yourself eyes to see." Whenever architects design bridges, they take into account what is known as the stress factor. Some flexibility is built into the bridge structure so that loads of all weights can be accommodated. If you, as a manager, are going to survive you must do the same with your style of management, your job descriptions, and your own philosophical viewpoint.

The times mandate that we know and understand ourselves and those with whom we work. There are so many external pressures tugging at us that are beyond our control and can greatly influence our decisions. Being sensitive to the existence of different value systems, and the way in which they may cause a blindspot to our own strengths and weaknesses, requires a conscious and persistent effort on the part of the manager. It is a monumental task, but it can be accomplished. Doing so will serve both you the manager and your subordinates.

REFERENCES

Beck, D. E. (1981, December). Bridging value systems to manage and motivate people. *Associated Management*, pp. 85–86.

Mali, P. (1981). *Management handbook: Operating guidelines, techniques and practices* (pp. 1393–1404). New York: Wiley.

Rorick, W. G. (1984). *The brain workshop handbook*. Boston: The Brain Company, Inc.

Spector, R. E. (1979). *Cultural diversity in health and illness* (pp. 76–84). New York: Appleton-Century-Crofts.

Table 1.2.
How to Work with Employees with Different Value Systems

Employee's Value System	Job Design	Growth Opportunities	Leadership Style	Performance Review
System 2: Tribalistic	Do be benevolent, protective, and autocratic. Don't impose planning and controlling onto "doing."	Do give guidance for advancement. Don't require or expect long-range career planning.	Do be a friendly decision maker and give reassurance that all is O.K. Don't be "iffy," intellectual, or use strange terms.	Do closely tie in the review with day-to-day performance. Don't try to tie review to the company's long-range plans and goals.
System 3: Egocentric	Do make subordinate feel extremely important and powerful. Don't fail to keep subordinate busy and under control.	Do make promotion contingent on good performance. Don't let subordinate "con" you or take advantage of other employees.	Do be tough, aggressive, and assume subordinate doesn't want to work. Don't be soft indecisive, or cause suspicion.	Do define specifically the individual advantages of daily performance. Don't relate performance to the work group.
System 4: Conformist	Do write detailed job descriptions and duties. Don't let subordinate lose sight of priorities, and don't expect creativity.	Do provide step-by-step normal career paths. Don't promote until subordinate feels he or she has earned it through hard work.	Do be straight, businesslike, respectful, and well organized. Don't be slick, profane, or disrespectful of tradition.	Do show logical connection of the review procedure to company policy. Don't be casual, loose, or unclear about expected performance.

System				
System 5: Manipulative	Do turn work into a management-by-objectives game. Don't fail to specify constraints and limits, and audit occasionally.	Do let subordinate run the corporate maze and leave room for "wheeling and dealing." Don't plan subordinate's career goals or use a structured system.	Do stress rewards and status and relate to subordinate's career goals. Don't force subordinate to follow company policy and procedure.	Do stress personal career advancement opportunities. Don't get into win–lose games or tell subordinates what to do.
System 6: Sociocentric	Do humanize work and promote group interaction. Don't let participation overshadow productivity.	Do provide "helping" opportunities and exposure to more people. Don't create competition or use the "carrot-and-stick" method.	Do be human, equal, and gain personal acceptance. Don't use power politics or manipulation.	Do illustrate how the review process helps people express themselves. Don't overstress individual performance or let the clock control discussions.
System 7: Existential	Do provide guidelines only, and involve subordinates in problem solving. Don't expect blind obedience or fail to get clear commitment.	Do provide movement in any direction. Don't be surprised if subordinate refuses a financial promotion to "do his or her own thing."	Do give subordinate access to information and let him or her make the decisions. Don't tell subordinate what to do or shut off questions	Do act as a resource, and let subordinate participate in the system design. Don't use top management to sell the importance of the review concept.

From Mali, P. (1981). Management handbook: Operating guidelines, techniques and practices (pp. 1393–1404). New York: Wiley.

2

Cultural Considerations

According to the experts, 90% of our mistakes in business will be made in judgments about people. You can narrow the odds and lessen this percentage by considering the cultures and subcultures of your environment.

We live in a pluralistic society, and it is imperative that we develop the ability to function within a range of cultures. People should not have to give up their identity to be a team player. As Dr. Ray Winbush of Vanderbilt University says in a University recruitment brochure, "We need to get away from the melting pot idea and think of the salad bowl concept instead. You don't have to relinquish your identity in a tossed salad. Every piece is distinct. A salad that's all lettuce or carrots is no good. It tastes better if there's a variety and a mixture there."

Like a good salad, every culture requires some essential ingredients:

1. A culture is a universal experience.
2. Each culture is unique to its particular group.
3. A culture is stable but not static.
4. A culture encompasses and largely determines one's life, yet it is rarely consciously noted.
5. A culture is a way of life for a group's values, attitudes, and beliefs, using the heritage of its constituents to maintain its stability.
6. All cultures have a language, which includes the spoken word, art forms, games, and rituals (Freeley, 1984).

To understand another person's culture, an interdisciplinary perspective must be employed. To view any one aspect of the culture is

9

to be myopic, and you will only have a partial picture. Areas to be considered in your study take on a theoretical form such as that developed by Banks (1987) (Figure 2.1). To further your understanding, you should establish what is fact and what is myth. There is no magical way to do this. Simply take a close look at cultural and ethnic groups and take inventory. The ethnic literacy test (Figure 2.2) is a good initial assessment tool for an individual or a group (Banks, 1987). The usual conclusion from this exercise is that there is more fiction than fact floating around. These untruths are often used as a basis of operation, and often determine our treatment of individuals,

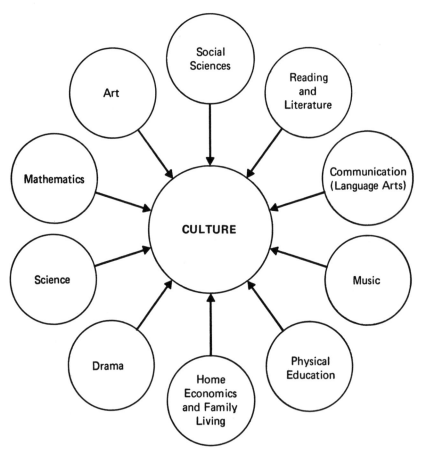

Figure 2.1. Studying culture from an interdisciplinary perspective. (From James A. Banks, Teaching Strategies for Ethnic Studies, Fourth Edition. Copyright © 1987 by Allyn and Bacon. Reprinted with permission.)

Ethnic Literacy Test

Directions: Indicate whether each of the following statements is TRUE or FALSE by placing a "T" or "F" in the space preceding it.

1 _____ The percentage of whites in the United States, relative to nonwhites, decreased between 1970 and 1980.

2 _____ The first Chinese immigrants who came to the United States worked on the railroads.

3 _____ In 1980, there were more than 26 million Afro-Americans in the United States.

4 _____ Puerto Ricans on the island of Puerto Rico became United States citizens in 1920.

5 _____ Between 1970 and 1979, the Mexican-American population increased by slightly more than 60 percent.

6 _____ Between 1820 and 1930, 15 million immigrants came to the United States.

7 _____ White Anglo-Saxon Protestants are the most powerful ethnic group in the United States.

8 _____ Rosh Hashanah, which in Hebrew means "end of the year," is a Jewish holiday that comes early in the fall.

9 _____ Between 1820 and 1971, Germans were the largest European group immigrating to the United States.

10 _____ The first law to limit immigration to the United States was passed in 1882 to restrict the number of African immigrants.

11 _____ Puerto Ricans in New York City tend to identify strongly with Afro-Americans in that city.

12 _____ Between 1820 and 1971, more individuals from Canada and Newfoundland immigrated to the United States than from Mexico.

13 _____ Most Afro-Americans came from the eastern parts of Africa.

14 _____ The internment of the Japanese Americans during World War II was opposed by President Franklin D. Roosevelt.

15 _____ In 1980, there were more than 14 million Hispanic Americans in the United States.

16 _____ More than 270,000 immigrants came to the United States from the Philippines between 1971 and 1980.

17 _____ Congress passed a Removal Act that authorized the removal of Indians from east to west of the Mississippi in 1830.

18 _____ A Japanese settlement was established in California as early as 1869.

19 _____ The United States acquired a large part of Mexico's territory under the terms of the Treaty of Guadalupe Hidalgo in 1848.

20 _____ Agriculture dominates the economy of the island of Puerto Rico.

21 _____ The first blacks to arrive in North America came on a Dutch ship that landed at Jamestown, Virginia, in 1619.

22 _____ Ethnic minorities made up about 17 percent of the United States population in 1980.

23 _____ *Paper sons* is a custom that is associated with Chinese Americans.

24 _____ In 1980, there were about one and a half million American Indians, Eskimos, and Aleuts in the United States.

25 _____ Some of the bloodiest riots involving Afro-Americans and whites occurred in the early 1900s.

(Continued)

Figure 2.2. An assessment of ethnic literacy. (From Banks, J. A. (1984). *Teaching strategies for ethnic studies* (3rd ed.). Boston: Allyn and Bacon.)

26 _____ More than 110,000 Vietnamese immigrated to the United States between 1971 and 1980.
27 _____ The United States acquired the island of Puerto Rico from Spain in 1898.
28 _____ There are only 438 Japanese surnames.
29 _____ Chinese immigrants to the United States became distinguished for their outstanding work on truck farms.
30 _____ The only large Puerto Rican community on the United States mainland is in New York City.
31 _____ A third-generation Japanese American is called a *Sansei.*
32 _____ More than 26 million Iranians immigrated to the United States between 1971 and 1980.
33 _____ More than one half of American Indians lived in central cities in 1980.
34 _____ Most Chinese immigrants to the United States came from western China.
35 _____ Eleven Italian Americans were lynched in New Orleans in 1892.
36 _____ Nativism directed against southern and eastern European immigrants was intense when the Statue of Liberty was dedicated in 1886.
37 _____ In 1980 there were more than three-quarters of a million Cubans living in the United States.
38 _____ More than 43,000 Haitians immigrated to the United States between 1971 and 1980.

Answers to Ethnic Literacy Test

1. T	2. F	3. T	4. F	5. T	6. F	7. T	8. F	9. T
10. F	11. F	12. T	13. F	14. F	15. T	16. T	17. T	18. T
19. T	20. F	21. F	22. T	23. T	24. T	25. T	26. T	27. T
28. F	29. F	30. F	31. T	32. T	33. T	34. F	35. T	36. T
37. T	38. T							

Figure 2.2 *(continued).*

whether consciously or unconsciously. We have all been programmed as children, and the programmers may not have had all their facts straight. Like a computer, if wrong data are put in, wrong answers are produced.

So far the discussion has focused on culture as a part of people's background. This is one way to view the topic. The other is to consider organizations as cultures themselves.

Every organization has a culture. If you listen to employees of the same organization you can get clues that will help you identify the culture. There is usually a phrase—a one-liner—that people use to describe the inner workings of the organization. For example, "this place is a jungle," or "this place is a zoo," or even "we are just one big happy family."

Notice the dress code, office decorum, annual events, whether ethnic jokes are told, and how information is communicated. Policies and procedures will tell you a great deal, too. Watch the status symbols displayed, and listen to the war stories passed along by senior staff members.

Organizations with strong cultures have several common characteristics:

1. They control their human resources with a heavy hand.
2. They limit who is let into the group.
3. They develop their people.
4. They reward their personnel.

For an organization, the culture serves four purposes:

1. It conveys a sense of identity for the members.
2. It facilitates the generation of commitment to something larger than the organization.
3. It enhances social system identity.
4. It serves as a sense-making device that guides and shapes behavior (del Bueno & Freund, 1986).

Organizations within organizations can have their own cultures, often referred to as subcultures. Because nursing organizations usually have the largest number of members, it is important to identify their culture. Deal and Kennedy (1982) have defined the culture of a nursing service organization as "the way we do things around here." In addition, there are five common elements:

1. Environmental variables:
   • Competitive arena, in both fiscal and quality measures
   • Diverse client population with diverse needs
   • Reimbursement issues
   • Continuous changes and improvements in technology
   • Mix of services provided
   • Mix of professional and nonprofessional staff
   • Staffing patterns
   • Bargaining units
2. Values
3. Heroes—individuals who:
   • Are the role models
   • Set standards of performance
   • Motivate others
   • Help to maintain the specialness of the organization

4. Rites and rituals
5. The cultural network—how the previous four elements are communicated (Ramirez, 1990).

W. Edwards Deming (1986) in his book, *The Deming Management Model*, identifies characteristics of strong and weak cultures:

Weak Cultures	Strong Cultures
Work frequently done in a confused manner	Caring leaders
No consistency in work standards	Vision of the future
More attention paid to work completion than to quality	Flexibility
Priorities changed constantly and communicated to members	Organizational mission
Slow decision-making process	Participative decision making

A simple exercise (Figure 2.3) may help you assess your corporate cultural weaknesses and strengths. Individual ratings of 3 or below show a need for improvement. Total scores of 80+ indicate a strong positive culture; scores of 60–70 indicate a need for culture building; and scores below 50 indicate a need for significant improvement. Weak cultures have an inhibiting nature about them; strong ones, a liberating nature. As stated by del Bueno and Freund (1986):

> Whether one treats the culture as a background factor, an organizational variable, or as a metaphor for conceptualization, the idea of culture focuses attention on the expressive, nonrational qualities of the organization and legitimates attention to its subjective, interpretive aspects. (p. 11)

Not everything about an organization is tangible—something you can put your hands on. We must learn to celebrate our diversity rather than be irritated by it. We must learn to appreciate our differences rather than ignore them. We must have as our foremost managerial goal the achievement of a fit between the cultural subsystems within the organization.

Your Culture Is Showing

Rate on a scale of 1–5 (5 = almost always; 4 = usually; 3 = sometimes; 2 = seldom; 1 = never)

In our company

_____ The mission statement is the heartbeat of the organization; it outlines the values, such as quality and commitment to excellence.

_____ The work environment is characterized by unity of purpose.

_____ There is mission training.

_____ The organization is an integrated whole.

_____ People have a clear vision of the future of the organization.

_____ People "know how things are done."

_____ There is cross-functional communication.

_____ There is cross-functional problem solving.

_____ The environment is prepared for change.

_____ Management and employees exemplify the corporate philosophy.

_____ The organization is committed to quality of service.

_____ A generally "happy and good" attitude prevails.

_____ There is strong leadership.

_____ Leadership is "caring and sensitive."

_____ Competence and superior performance are recognized.

_____ Applicants are screened to "fit" the organization's philosophy.

_____ Employees are "retrieved or terminated" if they do not emulate values, purpose, and mission of the organization.

_____ Management and employees are accountable; there is no "buck passing."

_____ Management spends time greeting and talking to employees.

_____ All positions are viewed as serving the "front line."

_____ **Total points**

State the basic elements of your organization's mission statement (including ideals, values, beliefs, and purpose): _____

Figure 2.3. An assessment of corporate culture. (From Human Resources Management Associates, Madera, CA, 1988.)

REFERENCES

Banks, J. A. (1987). *Teaching strategies for ethnic studies* (4th ed.). Boston: Allyn and Bacon.

Deal, T., & Kennedy, H. (1982). *Corporate cultures*. Menlo Park, CA: Addison-Wesley.

del Bueno, D., & Freund, C. (1986). *Power and politics in nursing administration: A case book*. Owings Mills, MD: National Health Publishing.

Deming, W. E. (1986). *The Deming management model*. New York: Dodd Mead.

Freeley, E. M., et al. (1984). Fundamentals of nursing care. New York: D. Van Nostrand.

Ramirez, C. D. (1990, January). Culture in a nursing service organization. *Nursing Management, 21*(1), 14–17.

3

Your Style of Interaction

All individuals choose, both consciously and unconsciously, the pattern of their interactions. How do I make decisions? How do I implement a plan of action? The answers to these questions vary greatly depending on one's past successes and failures. This process of interacting is your management style and can be determined by studying your observable actions, or behavior. The focus is on behavior, not personality.

We base most of our general impressions about others on observable behavior. Usually we quickly conclude that the person is friendly, funny, serious, quiet, aggressive, unpleasant, or outgoing. We then tend to react according to our initial impression. If this initial impression is erroneous, we introduce barriers to effective communication and to our relationships. Knowledge about style of interaction provides us with options for dealing with the behaviors we observe in others. This knowledge facilitates win–win relationships.

Your style of interaction is simply what you do—your observable behavior. The impact of this behavior on others is often significantly different from what you may expect. People respond to you according to what *they* perceive, not what you think they perceive.

The formula for effectively dealing with people is:

1. Know your style of interaction, and how you *affect* others.
2. Know the style of interaction of others, and their *needs*.
3. Develop *adaptability* in working with others.

Dimensions of Human Behavior

It is often said that there are no new ideas, just a recycling of ideas that sound different. This is certainly true when considering works that describe observable human behavior. Most are a blend of previous work, with a personal touch by the author(s) that gives them a slightly different thrust. In reviewing the literature you will frequently come across the names Hersey, Blanchard (Hersey & Blanchard, 1982), Likert, Geier, and Marston (Marston, 1979). Most of these authors identify two dimensions of human behavior: the level of boldness that we observe in ourselves and others, and the level of formality. All of us exhibit some degree of each. The more the manager understands these two dimensions, the easier it will be to develop effective working relationships and to gain understanding about the manner in which individuals perceive their environment and why they behave as they do.

In understanding human behavior, it is important to learn to increase the reliability of your perceptions about another person's behavior. As you increase the accuracy of your perceptions of someone else, you will also increase your effectiveness in working with that person successfully (Rife, 1989). Some dimensions of observable behavior that can be useful to you are included under two broad headings: boldness and formality.

Boldness is defined as the perceived effort a person makes to influence or control the thoughts and actions of others. A bold person is one who speaks out, makes strong statements, takes charge, and is forward and demanding. Boldness is characterized by telling or directing. On the opposite end of the continuum is an easygoing person who may be described as quiet, unassuming, cooperative, a good listener, and one who lets others take charge. Easygoing behavior is characterized by asking or questioning.

boldness

(Easygoing) Asks ————————> ————————**Tells (Bold)**

Specific Observable Behavior

Easygoing (Asks)	Bold (Tells)
Apologetic	Boisterous
Quiet	Bold
Shy	Outspoken

(Continued)

Easygoing (Asks)	Bold (Tells)
Moderate opinions	Talkative
Go-along attitude	Strong opinions
Likeable first impression	Quick decisions
Tends to avoid use of power	Take-charge attitude
Lets others take initiative	Overwhelming first impression
Asks questions	Tends to use power
Talks slowly	Makes statements
	Acts quickly

Observable Behavior for the Boldness Dimension

Boldness—The perceived effort one makes to control the thoughts or actions of others.

Low $\longleftarrow$ **boldness** $\longrightarrow$ **High**

Easygoing	Bold
Slow, deliberate speech	Fast, quick pace
Gestures tend to be close to body (arm muscles relaxed)	Gestures tend to be bold (arm muscles tight)
Asks rather than tells	Tells rather than asks
Chin, eyes down	Chin up, leans forward
Sits or stands at angle	Direct eye contact
Leans back	Sits or stands directly across
	Shoulders back
	Tone of voice is definite
	Up-front, to-the-point, firm handshake

Formality is defined as the perceived effort a person makes to control his or her emotions when relating to others. An informal person is one who reacts easily and openly to surrounding influences, appeals, and stimulations. Informal behavior is characterized as *experiencing* and *expressing* feelings and emotions. A formal person is one who is perceived as cool, unemotional, and businesslike, and tends to restrict any show of emotions. A formal person is characterized as *controlling* feelings and emotions. This does not mean that formal individuals are emotionless. They just tend not to express their emotions.

responsiveness

Formal ——————————> —————————— **Informal**

Specific Observable Behavior

Formal	Informal
Cautious	Emotional
Serious	Lighthearted
Intellectual	Happy-go-lucky
Formal dress and/or speech	Informal dress and/or speech
Secretive, cautious communicator	Open, impulsive communicator
	Dramatic opinions and actions
Measured opinions and actions	Permissive, fluid actions
Strict, disciplined attitudes	Emotional or impulsive decision making
Fact-oriented decision making	
Difficult to get to know	Easygoing with self and others
Demanding of others and self	Personal and friendly
Impersonal and businesslike	

Observable Behavior for the Formality Dimension

Formality—The perceived effort one makes to control emotions when relating to others.

formality

Control <—————————— ——————————> **Emote**

Formal	Informal
Little use of eyebrows, forehead, eyes, lips to communicate feelings about beliefs	Shares feelings
	Likes talking with people
	Palms of hands tend to be facing body
Tends to use short deliberate sentences	Large, flowing gestures (tend to flow wider than shoulders)
Eye searching, penetrating, serious	Open to touching (hand on shoulder, arms, or knee; hugs)

(Continued)

Formal	Informal
Little use of hands	Open, easy to talk to, frequently
Palms tend to be out when	side-tracks
hands used	Smiles easily
Gestures tend to be within	Maximum use of eyebrows,
width of shoulders	eyes, lips, cheeks to
Limited touching	communicate feelings about
Desires facts	beliefs
Slow to smile	
Seems guarded	

The boldness and formality dimensions of behavior are *independent* of each other. When placed together they form a pattern of behavior. Because each dimension is independent of the other, the patterns of behavior become easily observable. These patterns are the basis of your interaction style. Four basic styles of interaction emerge:

- A person who is bold and informal
- A person who is bold and formal
- A person who is easygoing and informal
- A person who is easygoing and formal

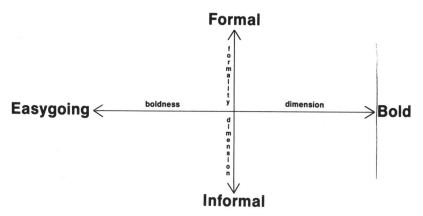

Though we all have some characteristics of each of the basic styles (that is, most people do not operate from just one style), we do tend to operate from one style more often than the other three. It is not unusual for a person to use one style predominantly at work and another in his or her personal relationships.

Behavioral Tendencies

Having a good understanding of the four basic interaction styles will provide you with the knowledge you need to develop more productive and effective relationships with people. Based on this knowledge, and on your observation skills, you will be able to anticipate the behavior of others in a variety of situations.

We tend to like those who are similar to us and dislike or avoid those who are the opposite. This is a reflection of our style of interaction. We see and judge other people based on our frame of reference. In order to develop a productive relationship with an individual who has a style different from ours, we must understand that person's style. Equally important, we must utilize our versatility in meeting that person's needs as well as our own.

We often decide that we like or dislike someone and then find reasons to support our decision. It is therefore important that we learn to separate our personal feelings about or reaction to that person from our description of that person's behavior.

A Major Focus for Each Style of Interaction

A consistent perception or focus runs through the actions of each person and usually typifies that person's basic style of interaction. This focus makes it possible for you to predict how people of a given style will most likely act in a wide variety of situations.

For the results-oriented (bold and formal) person, the focus is on *results:* he or she works within an immediate time frame, enjoys conflict, is a "big picture" thinker, and does not require personal feedback. The people-oriented (bold and informal) person focuses on *people:* he or she depends on intuition, is highly verbal, is overly optimistic, and wants recognition. The security-oriented (easygoing and informal) person focuses on *relationships:* he or she puts relationships first, provides services and accomplishes tasks, avoids conflict, and needs feedback. Finally, for the task-oriented (easygoing and formal) person, the focus is on *task:* he or she wants data, makes logical decisions, likes information in writing, and is uncomfortable with public recognition.

Typical Behavior

Each style of interaction offers clues that allow positioning on the boldness and formality dimensions of behavior. Positioning is a means of determining whether a person is bold or easygoing, formal or informal.

Results-oriented Manager

Swift reaction
Maximum effort to control
Minimum concern for relationships
Immediate time frame
Direct action
Tends to reject inaction

People-oriented Manager

Rapid reaction
Maximum effort to involve
Minimum concern for routine
Future time frame
Impulsive action
Tends to reject isolation

Security-oriented Manager

Unhurried reactions
Maximum effort to relate
Minimum concern for effecting change
Current time frame
Supportive action
Tends to reject conflict

Task-oriented Manager

Slow reaction
Maximum effort to organize
Minimum concern for relationships
Historical time frame
Cautious action
Tends to reject involvement

Interaction style is a matter of degree. Everyone will demonstrate some behavior characteristics of each of the basic interaction styles. However, most people will reflect one of the four basic styles more often than any of the other three.

Characteristic Behaviors of Each Style

Results-oriented Managers

1. They give the appearance of knowing what they want, and seem to display little difficulty expressing their conclusions about anything that concerns them.

2. The following slogan often applies: "Let's get it done and get it done now."
3. They tend to focus primarily on the immediate time frame, with little concern for the past.
4. Their responses appear swift, efficient, and to the point. They know what they want and become impatient with delays.
5. They appear to show little concern for the feelings of others or for personal relationships. Some may consider results-oriented managers' actions to be harsh, severe, or critical, since they seem to give such limited attention to relationships. Others may consider this behavior efficient, decisive, and action-oriented, providing the direction needed.
6. They seek control through the use of power. They often do so when they perceive power as a means to an end.

Observable behaviors displayed by these managers may be described as follows:

Restless
Competitive
Independent
Adventurous
Tend to be dominant
Strong-willed
Assertive
Want immediate results
Self-reliant
Cause action
Vigorous
Like power and authority
Like prestige and challenge
Want freedom from control and supervision
Want direct answers
Pioneering
Outspoken
Decisive
Persistent
Argumentative

People-oriented Managers

1. They frequently seem to spend much of their time and efforts moving toward a dream for the future.
2. This tendency causes some such managers to react in flighty,

impractical, or emotional ways. Managers who are highly people-oriented can work up excitement in others about the future.

3. It is easy for them to skip from one idea or activity to another, seeming to be impatient to find the most exciting vision of the moment.

4. Their behavior can become intensely stimulating, exciting, and fun for others who get caught up in their dreams.

5. They focus their attention on the future with intuitive visions and with their natural outspokenness. Thus, they may appear more imaginative and creative with their ideas than do managers operating under different styles.

6. It is also easy for them to make mistakes because they act out opinions, hunches, and intuitions, rather than deal with the harsh reality of hard facts.

Observable behaviors displayed by these managers may be described as follows:

Tend to be exciting and stimulating
Inspiring
Generate enthusiasm
Convincing
Often dramatic
Confident
Open and friendly toward others
Charming
Like working with people
Desire to help others
Playful
Like participating in groups
Persuasive
Want freedom of expression
Want freedom from detail
Like stimulating ideas
Like change
Optimistic
Talkative
Like recognition for accomplishments

Security-oriented Managers

1. The steadiness style is relationship-oriented. These managers interpret their environment personally and get involved in feelings and relationships between people. They frequently speculate on "who did what to whom and why."

2. They look for personal motives in the actions of others. They may find it difficult to believe that some people react purely from a personal principle or practicality, or simply from a desire to make the future sound more exciting.
3. Because they are concerned about how others feel and relationships between people, these managers can often lend joy, warmth, and freshness to a social situation.
4. Managers displaying a situational-oriented style can also appear slow or reluctant to change opinions that hold personal meaning for them.
5. They frequently stick with the comfortable known and tend to avoid decisions that might involve the risk of having to deal with people's reactions.

Observable behaviors displayed by these managers may be described as follows:

Dislike conflict
Patient with others
Thorough
Generous
Take time to listen
Demonstrate loyalty
Considerate of others' needs
Like security and stability
Like status quo unless given reason for change
Allow minimal work infringement on home life
Expect credit for work accomplished
Lenient
Obedient
Accommodating
Neighborly
Take time to make decisions
Want guarantee before change
Want others to agree
Want to be appreciated

Task-oriented Managers

1. These persons live life according to the facts, principles, logic, and consistency to be found in reality.
2. Because these managers tend to behave in ways that fit into their overall theory and ideas about the world, others may view them as lacking in enthusiasm or appearing cold or detached.

3. They project the image of great planners, organizers, and problem solvers, with the ability to work out a task systematically from beginning to end.
4. Because of their concern for facts and logical, serious, consistent organization of thought, coupled with a desire to be "right," task-oriented managers may sometimes be reluctant to declare a personal point of view.
5. They have a need to analyze all significant possibilities in an attempt to avoid any chance of making an illogical or inconsistent decision.
6. Facts, logic, and faith in principles appear to assume greater importance than personal friendships or personal gratification.

Observable behaviors displayed by these managers may be described as follows:

Orderly
Cautious
Perform precise work
Like controlled circumstances
Diplomatic
Like assurance of security
Utilize critical thinking
Soft-spoken
Follow directives and standards prescribed
Like status quo, unless assured of quality control
Prefer no sudden or abrupt changes
Harmonious
Check for accuracy
Humble
Obliging
Tend to be serious and persistent
Respectful
Devout
Well-disciplined
Agreeable

An Assessment of Managerial Style

You can begin to validate your style (see Figure 3.1) by using the following checklist. The style with the most checks is the one that you gravitate toward and use the most. You can also use this list to identify the style of others.

Behavioral Characteristics Rating Form

Name of person being rated _____
Directions: Circle one of the numbers to indicate how you see the person you are rating. For example:

Ask   1 2 ③ 4   Tell

The rater here decided the person being rated was more a "telling" person than an "asking" person, but not "telling" enough to rate a 4.

1. Reserved	1	2	3	4	Appears confident
2. Aggressive	1	2	3	4	Passive
3. Self-controlled	1	2	3	4	Responsive
4. Dominant	1	2	3	4	Easygoing
5. Goes along	1	2	3	4	Takes charge
6. Informal	1	2	3	4	Formal
7. Spontaneous	1	2	3	4	Disciplined
8. Hesitant communicator	1	2	3	4	Communicates readily
9. Challenging	1	2	3	4	Accepting
10. Appears organized	1	2	3	4	Appears unorganized
11. Lets other initiate	1	2	3	4	Initiates social contact
12. Makes statements	1	2	3	4	Asks questions
13. Shy	1	2	3	4	Overbearing
14. Fun-loving	1	2	3	4	Reserved
15. Appears thoughtful	1	2	3	4	Appears active
16. Assertive	1	2	3	4	Relaxed
17. Expresses feeling	1	2	3	4	Witholds feeling
18. Task-oriented	1	2	3	4	Relationship-oriented
19. Gentle	1	2	3	4	Pushy
20. Impulsive	1	2	3	4	Discriminating
21. Introvert	1	2	3	4	Extrovert
22. Cool	1	2	3	4	Warm
23. Direct	1	2	3	4	Subtle
24. Close	1	2	3	4	Distant
25. Saves opinions	1	2	3	4	States opinions
26. Talkative	1	2	3	4	Quiet (Continued)

Figure 3.1. Behavioral characteristics rating form and score sheet. (From Rife, L. G. (1989). *Organizational effectiveness through human engineering: A training program. Unpublished seminar.*)

The Results-oriented Manager

Restless
Vigorous
Competitive
Likes power and authority
Independent
Likes prestige and challenge
Adventurous
Wants freedom from control and supervision

Behavioral Characteristics Score Sheet

To locate the person on the boldness scale: place the ratings from the Behavioral Characteristics Rating Form on the lines following the corresponding question numbers below:

1. _____	2. _____
5. _____	4. _____
8. _____	9. _____
11. _____	12. _____
13. _____	16. _____
15. _____	23. _____
19. _____	26. _____
21. _____	
25. _____	
Sum #1 _____	Sum #2 _____

(Sum #1) + 35 − (Sum #2) = _____ divided by 16 = _____

Place an X on the following scale corresponding to the score above.

Easygoing   Bold
1.00   1.75   2.50   3.25   4.00

To locate the person on the formality scale: place the ratings from the Behavioral Characteristics Rating Form on the lines following the corresponding question numbers below:

6. _____	3. _____
7. _____	10. _____
14. _____	18. _____
17. _____	22. _____
20. _____	
24. _____	
Sum #1 _____	Sum #2 _____

(Sum #1) + 20 − (Sum #2) = _____ divided by 10 = _____

Place an X on the following scale corresponding to the score above.

Informal   Formal
1.00   1.75   2.50   3.25   4.00

Figure 3.1 (*continued*).

Tends to be dominant
Wants direct answers
Strong-willed
Pioneering
Assertive
Outspoken
Wants immediate results
Decisive
Self-reliant

Persistent
Causes action
Argumentative

The People-oriented Manager

Tends to be exciting and stimulating
Playful
Likes participating in groups
Inspiring
Persuasive
Generates enthusiasm
Wants freedom of expression
Convincing
Wants freedom from detail
Often dramatic
Likes stimulating ideas
Confident
Likes change
Open and friendly toward others
Optimistic
Charming
Talkative
Likes working with people
Likes recognition for accomplishments
Desires to help others

The Security-oriented Manager

Dislikes conflict
Allows minimal work infringement on home life
Patient with others
Expects credit for work accomplished
Thorough
Lenient
Generous
Obedient
Takes time to listen
Accommodating
Demonstrates loyalty
Neighborly
Considerate of others' needs
Takes time to make decisions
Likes security and stability

Wants guarantee before change
Likes status quo unless given reason for change
Wants others to agree
Wants to be appreciated

The Task-oriented Manager

Orderly
Prefers no sudden or abrupt changes
Cautious
Harmonious
Performs precise work
Checks for accuracy
Likes controlled circumstances
Humble
Diplomatic
Obliging
Likes assurance of security
Tends to be serious and persistent
Utilizes critical thinking
Respectful
Soft-spoken
Devout
Follows directives and standards prescribed
Well-disciplined
Agreeable
Likes status quo, unless assured of quality control

Appropriate Managerial Behaviors

Appropriate Boldness

The degree of boldness of an individual is more the perception of others than self-perception. It is other people who àre most affected by your level of boldness. You can be unnecessarily or inappropriately bold. It is equally possible to be perceived as so easygoing that you seem submissive. Adaptability on the boldness scale is the ability to present the *appropriate* level of boldness in any given situation. Individuals with little adaptability in this area are those who tend to be consistently too bold or too easygoing.

Some Ways to Increase Boldness

1. ACT RATHER THAN REACT: Increasing boldness requires two levels of development that need to be experienced. The first is to feel

comfortable speaking up, and the second is to sound convincing. Offer your honest opinion on a subject at the first opportunity, and before someone asks you what you think. Be candid and frank. Don't wait until you are asked.

2. BE CREATIVE THROUGH BRAINSTORMING: A nonassertive person is often afraid to offer a differing opinion or idea for fear of causing a conflict. Presenting an idea that builds on an earlier one often produces the best idea of all. If you simply support others, nothing new will emerge. A conflicting idea can be offered without so much personal involvement that rejection of the idea feels like a rejection of the person. Think of your idea as a creation, not a conflict.

3. VALUE ENOUGH TO DISAGREE: "I don't care what you say, just say something" is a plea from a person who is frustrated. The easygoing individual needs to know how discrediting it is to have an idea treated as irrelevant, such as when someone feels that you disagree but choose "not to say anything if I can't say something nice." Instead, show the person that you are interested in what he or she is talking about, even though you disagree with the position taken.

4. MANAGE CONFLICT, DON'T AVOID IT: A real step in the direction of integrating the skill of boldness is to dare to disagree and at the same time listen. Develop and use problem-solving skills rather than avoiding conflict.

5. BE FLEXIBLE—COMPROMISE PRECEDES PROGRESS: A person often has to give something up to get something better. Remember Aesop's fable about the crow and the fish. The crow would rather starve to death than let go of the fish. People who have a lot of technically correct information may have a more difficult time letting go of the need to be right than do others who know less. Go for the big picture and be willing to let go of some of the smaller, less important pieces. If the other person has to admit you are 100% right, there is not much room left for saving face. The chances of making an important impact on the solution increase in proportion to the respect the other person is able to give to your ideas.

6. INITIATE RATHER THAN AVOID CHANGE: Take less time to make a decision; require less information. Initiate several low-risk changes and build your confidence. If 50% of your decisions are right, you will be above average as a decision maker.

Some Ways to Moderate Boldness

Pushing others into actions or decisions is often perceived as manipulative and/or controlling. If you have received evidence that others see you as too confrontational or controlling, the following may be incorporated into your personal plan.

1. ASK, DON'T ASSUME: The bold individual is most familiar with the role of telling. Asking questions and becoming skillful at helping the other person arrive at a conclusion that you have already reached is a more subtle approach to your common goal.

2. ADMIT: *No one is always right.* The skill of admitting you are wrong or that you do not have a solution or answer can be expressed in a positive way through the use of the word "and." When one says, "I was wrong, but . . ." or "I don't know, but . . ." the conjunction "but" negates the first half of the sentence and often causes defensive reactions in the listener. Use of the word "and" eases the person into a problem-solving attitude where one can help rather than oppose. Try to eliminate words that cause other people to feel defensive.

3. ACTIVELY LISTEN: Sometimes the bold person states a position and then says, "No further discussion is needed." Giving another individual the time to say something is not enough. A bold individual needs to listen with the other person's frame of reference clearly in mind. Good communication includes acknowledging the merits of the other person's view. It means asking enough questions and trying to rephrase any response in order to understand exactly what the other person is trying to say (i.e., "Are you saying that . . . ?" or "Do you mean . . . ?"). Bold people often think that they already know what someone is trying to say, and the person often feels "unheard." Check out what you think the person meant, then incorporate what you can of his or her ideas into your position.

4. PAUSE AND REFLECT: A bold individual often believes that time is money. An air of *impatience* and *restlessness* is conveyed whenever he or she interacts with a person of a different style. *To slow down and give the other person time* often has the surprising result of your learning or receiving something valuable. Perhaps even more important is the development of trust, respect, and support. Nonverbal clues to impatience include: looking at your watch, accepting phone calls during a meeting, signing correspondence, reading mail, picking lint off clothing.

5. AVOID OVERWHELMING: Overwhelming others with your capabilities and knowledge of a subject is often easy to do. Being bold does not give the other person many choices—and most people prefer to think that they have choices. If you learn to place an emphasis on problem solving, on making use of all the available resources, both human and material, then you will not create a dependency on just

you for answers. Instead of people feeling so overwhelmed that they cannot operate without you, they need to see you as one of several necessary and valuable resources.

6. MODERATE YOUR MANNER—GENTLENESS IS THE MARK OF A STRONG PERSON: Frequently, bold individuals have developed a loud tone that drowns out others. This is sometimes coupled with large physical size, and when the bold person is both big and loud, the easygoing individual feels intimidated. Slowing your pace of delivery and quieting your voice allows other people to be more vocal. This, in turn, increases your effectiveness because people enjoy meeting a strong, confident person who can put others at ease.

7. AVOID TALKING ABOUT ACCOMPLISHMENTS: In conversations, avoid the need to present your accomplishments and achievements.

Appropriate Formality

Some Ways to Improve Expressive Ability

The emotionally restrained individual believes that this behavior is the most rationally effective style, and it is difficult to present a logical argument for change. Motivation must come from elsewhere. Research does indicate, however, that the most effective individual is one who can display a maturity in judgment about the appropriateness of displaying feelings and can convey a warm acceptance to others without too much intimacy. The following suggestions will help to improve expressive ability.

1. LEARN TO USE YOUR RIGHT BRAIN: Split-brain research has shown that the left brain's functions are primarily rational, logical, sequential, and deductive, and the right brain's functions are intuitive, emotional, and inductive. Each person needs a balance of both aspects of brain function in order to be complete. Imbalanced behavior produces a less effective person. Don't allow the only emotion you experience each day to be negative, such as anger at the traffic or at the incompetencies of others. Think about one thing you can feel happy about, and clear some private time to experience your feelings.

2. EXPRESS YOUR EXPERIENCE: A highly effective person has good communication skills. This ability includes competence in speaking with highly emotional or relationship-oriented people. Though you may not be interested in other people's personal problems, it is of prime importance that you learn to accept their emotions.

3. RELATE PERSONAL GOALS TO JOB GOALS: When speaking to

people of other styles, be sure to give one or two examples that show personal application. Most people want involvement within the job. Many make this commitment only when they are involved at a personal level.

4. LEARN TO MAKE SMALL TALK: Since informal people want to feel personally recognized, *taking a little time to socialize is important*. Though social conversation may not meet your needs, it does meet the needs of *many others*.

5. EXPRESS FEELINGS: To express feelings you may have about an idea, you need to know what those feelings are. Getting in touch with feelings is not easy if you are used to thinking and expressing ideas rather than feelings. One communication skill is to say "I feel . . ." and say a feeling word, rather than "I feel that . . ." and say a thought.

6. LET OTHERS KNOW YOU: Considerable research has confirmed that people who withhold affection or deny themselves expression of emotions have a significantly higher rate of illness than those who express their emotions. Start slowly and minimize the risk. But learn to accept and express feelings and emotions. *This is not an indicator of weakness.*

Some Ways to Reduce Informality

1. LIMIT CONFIDENCES: Holding back an impulsive trust of people you have just met may give you a better perspective when you start to build a close relationship later. Too much information too soon can result in a lack of respect or trust.

2. FOCUS ON JOB OBJECTIVES: The informal person often zeros in on the feelings of others, or notices that someone looks tired or stressful. Too much attention to feelings reduces your job effectiveness.

3. MAINTAIN APPROPRIATE DISTANCE: If the informal person challenges and expects high performances from others, a measure of objectivity must prevail. If the informal person gets too close, some may take advantage of the relationship. A step in developing objectivity is to focus on the goal, with support taking the form of belief in the other's capabilities, rather than an inordinate amount of empathy.

4. INSIST ON RESULTS—THIS IS NOT REJECTION: The informal person wants to be liked. A step in the development of objectivity includes focusing on the action rather than the person. One often confuses the person and the action, and as a relationship-oriented person, you can confuse another's rejection of an action as rejection of you. Explaining the separation is helpful.

5. KNOW THE APPROPRIATE TIME FOR FEELINGS: *An effective* interested. Rather, you need to learn to control your feelings when you are dealing with highly objective individuals. Otherwise trust is likely to break down.

6. AVOID OVEREMOTING—IT IS VIEWED AS IMMATURE: A subjective expressive person is very much in touch with a full range of emotions. A free display of that temperament is viewed by others as inappropriate and childish.

Patterns of Failure and Patterns of Success of the Manager

Patterns of Failure

1. Avoids interpersonal relationship problems.
2. Tends to "wing it," rather than develop a plan or strategy.
3. Shows inappropriate attention to details.
4. Has no handle on priorities, tries to do everything.
5. Tends to move too slowly.
6. Lacks boldness, nerve, and self-confidence.
7. Tends to tolerate ineffective subordinates too long.
8. Does not seek advice or help.
9. Tends to have personal blind spots, e.g., a poor speaker who speaks a lot.

Patterns of Success

1. Deals well with interpersonal relationships.
2. Performs careful analysis of decisions and the impact of decisions.
3. Develops an operating strategy.
4. Recognizes classical dilemmas and handles "no-win" situations.
5. Uses a wide variety of techniques.
6. Changes style to fit the situation; is flexible and adaptable.
7. Motivates subordinates and satisfies superiors.
8. Manages him- or herself (Skinner & Sasser, 1977, pp. 141–145).

All managers have the same six reasons to manage: money, time, people, materials, space, and systems. The way we manage is based on whether our attention and style are focused on managing momentum—the day-to-day activities—or on managing potential—the future. Both styles are needed.

REFERENCES

Hersey, P., & Blanchard, K. (1982). *Management of organizational behavior utilizing human resources* (4th ed.). Englewood Cliffs, NJ: Prentice-Hall.

Marston, W. M. (1979). In J. G. Geier (Ed.), *Emotions of normal people, interpretive introduction*. Minneapolis: Persona Press.

Rife, L. G. (1989). *Organizational effectiveness through human engineering: A training program* (pp. 2-7–5-9). Unpublished seminar.

Skinner, W., & Sasser, W. E. (1977, November/December). Managers with impact: Versatile and inconsistent. *Harvard Business Review*, pp. 140–148.

4

Power and People

Words do not always mean the same thing to different people. S. I. HayaKawa (1978) says that "where we draw the line between one class of things and another depends upon the interests we have and the purposes of the classification. No classification is any more final than any of the others; each of them is useful for its purpose. For example; consider the word "cat." To a child this could be a kitten; to a construction worker, a large earth-moving machine; to a lion tamer, a large jungle animal; and to hospital personnel, it could refer to a CAT scanner.

A similar cadre of definitions occurs in discussions about "power." The very word conjures up energy-related synonyms such as influence, force, authority, and control. It is important to clarify what power is, how it is manifested, and how to identify its presence.

First, the terms authority, influence, force, and control cannot be used interchangeably. Neither are they synonymous with power, but they are related to power and how it works. Force is the application of sanctions. Authority is the right to apply those sanctions, and can be applied over people (supervised), over things (operational), and over agreements (commitment) (Axnick, 1981). Influence is having an impact on others. Power encompasses all of these, but its meaning can be distilled into one sentence best stated by Rogers (cited in Blanchard & Hersey, 1982): ". . . it is the potential for influence." It is something that we all possess, even though in most instances it is in a dormant state. Some basic principles can further delineate the parameters of power:

The Basic Principles of Power

1. Power is always relative.
2. Power may be real or apparent.
3. Power may be exerted without action.
4. Power is finite and thus limited.
5. Power exists to the extent that it is accepted.
6. The ends of power cannot be separated from the means.
7. The exercise of power always entails cost and risk.
8. Power relationships change over time.
9. If someone else has power, you do not have it for that given period of time.
10. If your power is legislated or negotiated away, it is no longer there (Karrass, 1970).

The fascination with power has entertained managers for years. Some have sought to classify the types of power in an attempt to understand it. Though there are numerous ways of doing this, the most frequently cited classification system was developed by French and Ramen in collaboration with Kruglanski, Hersey, and Goldson et al. (Blanchard & Hersey, 1982). The types of power are described as follows:

1. COERCIVE POWER is based on fear. A leader high in coercive power induces compliance because failure to comply will lead to punishment such as undesirable work assignments, reprimands, or dismissal.

2. LEGITIMATE POWER is based on the position held by the leader. Normally, the higher the position, the greater is the legitimate power. A leader high in legitimate power induces compliance or influences others because they feel that he or she has the right, by virtue of position in the organization, to expect that suggestions will be followed.

3. EXPERT POWER is based on the leader's possession of expertise, skill, and knowledge, which induce respect in and thus influence others. A leader high in expert power possesses the expertise to facilitate the work behavior of others. The respect leads to compliance with the leader's wishes.

4. REWARD POWER is based on the leader's ability to provide rewards for people who believe that compliance will lead to positive gains such as increased pay, promotion, or recognition.

5. REFERENT POWER is based on the leader's personal traits. A leader high in referent power is generally liked and admired by others

because of his or her personality. This liking for, admiration for, and identification with the leader influences others.

6. INFORMATION POWER is based on the leader's possession of or access to information that is perceived as valuable by others. This power base influences others because they need the information or want to be "in" on things.

7. CONNECTION POWER is based on the leader's having "connections," influential or important persons inside or outside the organization. A leader high in connection power induces compliance from others because they aim at gaining the favor, or avoiding the disfavor, of the powerful connection.

Also essential to the understanding of power is familiarity with the reasons why individuals go to others for decisions on work-related matters, and in so doing temporarily give or share their power with another. A study by Filley Grimes (cited in Blanchard & Hersey, 1982) gives 11 such reasons:

> These reasons, from most frequently to least frequently mentioned, were: responsibility and function (the person is responsible for the particular matter); formal authority (the person is in a position to make decisions generally); control of resources (the person controls money, information, etc.); collegial (a group of peers has the right to be consulted); manipulation (the person can get the decision made in the manner desired); default or avoidance (the person is available and will deal with the problem); bureaucratic rules (the rules specify the person to consult); traditional rules (custom, tradition, or seniority specify the person to consult); equity (the person is a fair decision maker); friendship (the person is personally liked); and expertise (the person has superior knowledge of the subject). (p. 178)[1]

Power has also been further divided into *personal power* and *position power*. This notion of personal power is worthy of some attention because it affects every encounter the manager has with others. Personal power in this instance means "the ability to integrate external power (the capacity to act) with internal power (the capacity to reflect) (Hagberg, 1989). This means none of us is without some degree of power. The more we know ourselves and are in tune with what we know, the more personal power we possess. The challenge is

---

[1] From Blanchard, K., & Hersey, P. (1982). *Management of organizational behavior.* Englewood Cliffs, NJ: Prentice-Hall. Reprinted by permission.

not to let this acquisition change us. According to Hagberg, personal power increases when you have both external and internal power.

A model of personal power has been developed that depicts its dimensions (Figure 4.1). You will notice several things as you study the model:

1. The stages are ordered from external to internal, and you move through them in the order given.

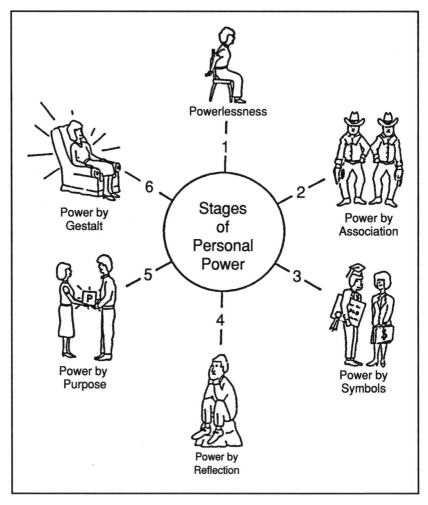

Figure 4.1   Stages of personal power. (From Hagberg, J. (1989). Personal power and the home healthcare nurse. *Home Health Care Nurse, 7*(3), 23–26.)

2. The stages are cumulative, each building upon its predecessor.
3. The higher stages are all related to internal power.

The six stages may be described briefly as follows:

Stage 1: *Powerlessness* occurs when individuals feel that things are happening to them, that they are victims and are dependent. Self-esteem is usually low.

Stage 2: *Power by association* can be described by "it's not what you know but who you know." The belief is that if you can get into the right circle, the power of others will soon rub off on you, either by your modeling behaviors or by studying behaviors that you wish to demonstrate.

Stage 3: *Power by symbols* is associated chiefly with material possessions such as status, compensation, titles, college degrees, etc. Many feel they have "arrived" at this point. The need for control of everything is an obsession.

Stage 4: *Power by reflection* is earmarked by a "journey" inward and a close examination of self. There is confusion about what rewards in life really matter.

Stage 5: *Power by purpose* is where the goal shifts to empowerment of others and the recognition of one's strengths and weaknesses. You recognize that you cannot be good at everything, and that nurturing the strength of others does not diminish who you are but exalts you.

Stage 6: *Power by Gestalt* is the stage at which one recognizes where true power resides, and as Martin Buber puts it, the "I" becomes "thou" (Hagberg, 1989).

Most of us occupy one of these stages the majority of the time. A big determinant of the stage is personal motives and self-esteem. Power motivators (those who influence) believe that their job is "not to force other people to do things, but to help them to figure out ways of getting their job done better for the company" (Hagberg, 1989). Power seekers, on the opposite side of the coin, always ask themselves and others, "What's in it for me? If I don't benefit, leave me out." Identifying where you are as a manager, and where those you supervise or work with are, can only enhance your knowledge of how to work effectively with others. Make no mistake: leaders who know how to get things done, says Robert E. Wood of the University of Maryland at College Park, all have one common characteristic—power. Those who are perceived as powerful possess three things: political savvy, an obvious power base and network, and more than their fair share of scarce resources (del Bueno & Freund, 1986).

To accumulate power, say del Bueno and Freund, you need three commodities: information, resources, and support. Politically you must be a strategist in the wise use of all three. The authors believe that the use of politics can help overcome bureaucratic constipation. The political strategies most often employed are: coalition forming, lobbying, increasing visibility, posturing or bluffing, and bargaining or trade offs. Those who are savvy vary the strategy and, as Machiavelli succinctly champions in *The Prince*, rely on what is in their power and not what is in the power of others. Perhaps the following story summarizes this fact best.

> During a hike in the woods a troop of boy scouts came across an abandoned section of railroad track. Each in turn tried walking the rails but eventually lost his balance and tumbled off.
>
> Suddenly two of the boys, after considerable whispering, offered to bet that they could both walk the entire length of the track without falling off. Challenged to make good their boast, the two boys jumped up on opposite rails, extended a hand to balance each other, and walked the entire section of track with no difficulty whatever.
>
> There, in a nutshell, is the principle of modern business and community living. The day of the hermit and the lone wolf are gone forever. We do things better by helping each other. The fellow who lends a helping hand benefits himself at the same time as he helps the other fellow.
>
> The reverse is also true. When we don't help each other, when we don't cooperate, the whole system starts to rattle and shake.
>
> The difference between a good company and a poor one, an effective department and an inefficient one, is often reflected in the cooperation, or lack of it, among the people who work there. When people help each other, freely and voluntarily, there's a spirit of teamwork that makes a department or company really go—a pleasure to be associated with. When there's no cooperation—no spirit of the helping hand freely given—what might have been pleasant jobs become grudging chores. (Tennessee Hospital Association, 1978)[2]

---

[2] From Tennessee Hospital Association. (1978, December). Decision-making. *The Nurse Manager*, 1(10), 10. Reprinted by permission.

REFERENCES

Axnick, K. J. (1981, July). *Infection Control Digest, 2*(7), 1.

Blanchard, K., & Hersey, P. (1982). *Management of organizational behavior.* Englewood Cliffs, NJ: Prentice-Hall.

del Bueno, D., & Freund, C. (1986). *Power and politics in nursing administration: A case book* (pp. 6–8). Owings Mills, MD: National Health Publishing.

Hagberg, J. (1989). Personal power and the home healthcare nurse. *Home Health Care Nurse, 7*(3), 23–26.

HayaKawa, S. I. (1978). *Language in thought and action* (4th ed.). New York: Harcourt Brace Jovanovich.

Karrass, C. L. (1970). *The negotiating game.* New York: Thomas Y. Crowell.

Tennessee Hospital Association. (1978, December). Decision-making. *The Nurse Manager, 1*(10), 10.

5

Leadership Styles

I am always entertained to hear armchair quarterbacks after Monday night football games, going over the plays and describing how they would do things differently if they were in charge—so many approaches and strategies! Without realizing it, these self-professed "pros" are revealing their preferences for leadership styles, the methods they would use without hesitancy to influence other people's behavior. This ritual of going over the plays indicates that we know deep down that we can be leaders if we care enough about the agenda. Some people can call up these leadership qualities more easily than others. Some must brush up on the technical aspects, but most of us can do the job required because we have all learned from ineffective leaders what not to do.

Many individuals are thrust into leadership roles because they were good followers in other situations. Some are considered for leadership positions because they are technically competent and articulate, have a larger-than-life persona, or are good with people. Many female or minority leaders feel that their demonstrated competencies were not as much a factor as their sex or race. Since today's cutting-edge companies want to have the appearance of being nondiscriminatory and equal-opportunity employers, they promote, hire, and seek women and minorities. Some leaders are promoted because of their longevity with the company, and the policy is to promote from within. Other organizations like to look outside for leadership in an attempt to minimize internal competition.

Regardless of how you got into your leadership position, you are there and what you don't know you can learn. Paul Cherrington states that "Incompetence is due almost entirely to lack of information—not a lack of quality." Information about what? Information about yourself, your strengths and weaknesses; the effects of leadership styles on work performance; the organizational goals; and the nature of people and how to treat them.

Sometimes people use the names "boss" and "leader" interchangeably, but they are not the same, as Fred Pryor, a noted management seminar leader, has lucidly explained:

Bosses versus Leaders

Bosses drive their people. . .
Leaders coach them.
Bosses inspire fear. . .
Leaders, enthusiasm.
Bosses say "Get here on time. . ."
Leaders, "Get there ahead of time."
Bosses fix the blame for the breakdown.
Leaders fix the breakdown.
Bosses say, "Go. . ."
Leaders say, "Let's go."
Bosses use people.
Leaders develop them.[1]

Fred Pryor

So the next time you hear someone exclaiming that you are too bossy, perhaps you are exhibiting a leadership style that intimidates rather than encourages.

All of us possess a leadership style; we have all attempted and succeeded at getting someone else to do something in an effort to meet a set goal. The method we most often use to influence the behavior of others is our primary leadership style. When this attempt is unsuccessful we go to a secondary style or styles, depending upon what has worked for us before. In all of our leadership encounters there is a leader and a follower. These assignments may be made formally or informally, and often the environment will dictate this.

A review of other authors shows a consensus that leadership styles fall under two broad categories: initiating structures and consideration structures. Initiating structures concentrate on the tasks at

---

[1] From Fred Pryor, Inc., Shawnee Mission, KS.

hand, whereas consideration structures focus on the relationship dimensions (Kison, 1989).

Hersey and Blanchard (1982) have defined four basic leadership styles. Two fall under the initiating structure and two under the consideration structure.

Style 1: *Telling*—Tell somebody what to do and watch them closely.
Style 2: *Selling*—Explain what you want somebody to do and let them ask clarifying questions.
Style 3: *Participating*—Share ideas and support the follower's efforts.
Style 4: *Delegating*—Turn over the responsibility and allow the subordinate to "run with the ball."

A style that is successfully used in one situation can be lethal in another.

First, say Oncken and Weiss (1974), you must identify on whose back the "monkey" resides—the monkey being the problem behavior that is to be influenced. These authors have identified four of the most likely scenarios. Combinations of these four can and do occur, but the leader usually gravitates toward one style that he or she is most comfortable using. Each style has a strength and a weakness, making it the most effective in certain situations and the least effective in others. You can learn to use all four styles so that you can select whatever the situation demands; the situation should dictate the leadership style. To select the correct style, the leader must diagnose the situation, then prescribe the treatment.

Syndrome 1: The leader has a "monkey." The leader sees the behavior of the follower as a problem, but the follower is not aware that a problem exists.
Treatment: Focus on the task and play down the relationship.

Syndrome 2: Both the leader and the follower have "monkeys." They both see the follower's behavior as unacceptable.
Treatment: Focus on the relationship and the task.

Syndrome 3: The follower has a "monkey." The follower's behavior is a problem to the follower only.
Treatment: Focus on the relationship and play down the task.

Syndrome 4: The "monkey" is up in a tree eating a banana because there is no problem.
Treatment: Leave things as they are.

All this monkey business is about you, the leader, empowering the workforce. In so doing, you support and encourage subordinates to take the reins of authority, and your time can be more efficiently used to create an environment that is conducive to peak performance. The empowerment of your subordinates increases their potential exposure to organizational conflict. More and more of your role will be as mediator—fostering cooperation and problem solving. Using a transactional analysis concept known as Karpman's triangle can be of invaluable assistance (Karpman, 1968). Get to know it intimately. It can bring order to chaos and give you a clear sense of direction. The triangle has three basic roles: victim, persecutor, and rescuer.

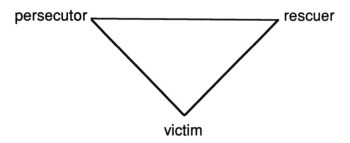

The victim is the person with the "monkey." The persecutor constantly puts down the monkey carrier. The rescuer comes to save the day and to solve the victim's problems.

Your role is to identify the characters and to create an environment for negotiation. Avoid being the persecutor or the rescuer, but simply attempt to be the ringside referee. As Greenbaugh of Dartmouth College says in a College recruitment brochure, "you want to instruct them to agree on a course of action that both can live with." You want the opportunity to listen and then to act. So be careful that you do not fall into the no-win roles.

Negotiation is nothing more than selling your point of view without the other party being aware of it. The steps are essentially:

1. Get the attention of the other party. You can do this by starting with the issue that is crucial to them.
2. Ask questions, and listen to responses to pick up subtleties.
3. Present the evidence for your point of view, keeping in mind what gets your opponent's ear.
4. Anticipate objections and have answers for them ready and waiting.

5. Close the sale. One of the best ways to do this is to list the positive and the negative aspects of what you have proposed. Start with the objections, then place the counterarguments on the positive side. The idea is to list more positives than negatives (Pell, 1989).

Additional points of refinement during family feuds or business roundtable negotiations are:

1. To help others save face, make the first concession.
2. Start off with the easy issues and work your way to the complicated ones.
3. Listen, listen, listen.
4. Have your trade-offs in mind so that when you hit a stalemate you will have carefully thought through what you can give up without the gnashing of teeth.
5. When possible, increase the number of options available to the other party.
6. Always strive for a win–win ending.

New-age skills for today's leader have been identified by Craig Hickman and Michael Silva (cited in Walls, 1989). As you look them over, note that facts and figures are not the focus—people skills and the ability to motivate others are. The following skills were listed:

Creative insight
Sensitivity to others
Vision of the future
Versatility
Focus
Patience

To get an idea about where you stand, take the inventory "Your Leadership is Showing" (Figure 5.1).

Adaptability

Being adaptable in relationships is the ability to meet another person's needs while taking care of your own needs. It is an important skill in management, supervision, and sales, and is equally important in personal relationships. In developing adaptability, you first need to know how your style of interaction tends to *affect* others. Then you must be able to assess the other person's basic style and to understand his or her psychological needs. Most often, adaptability simply requires the ability to increase or reduce boldness, or to increase or

---

Your Leadership is Showing

Rate yourself on a scale of 1–5 (5 = almost always; 4 = usually; 3 = sometimes; 2 = seldom; 1 = never).

As a leader I

_____ Emulate the values, philosophy, and purpose of the organizational mission.

_____ Demonstrate persistence and patience in achieving the mission.

_____ Ask people who report to me to participate in setting goals, priorities, deadlines, and in problem solving.

_____ Unconditionally accept employees, realizing everyone has certain limitations.

_____ Listen carefully to what people are saying.

_____ Remain equally open to facts and figures and feelings of others.

_____ Build relationships with other departments and organizations.

_____ Communicate with subordinates about expectations, standards, and policies.

_____ Give praise and recognition for a job well done.

_____ Create an environment of accessibility with supervisors, peers, and subordinates.

_____ Communicate the "vision" for all to understand and embrace.

_____ View issues and problems from many diverse perspectives.

_____ Easily change approaches to problem solving if one doesn't work.

_____ Encourage cross-functional problem solving.

_____ Encourage and reward new ideas from subordinates.

_____ Treat employees differently because of their individual differences.

_____ Know what inspires members of the work group.

_____ Have very few formal appointments and meetings.

_____ Enjoy coming to work and show it.

_____ Observe the environment to identify possible changes in customer (client) or competitor behaviors.

_____ Initiate new systems, models, and approaches as appropriate and/or needed.

_____ Give activities my full, undivided attention.

_____ Limit activities to those in which excellence is attainable.

_____ Exercise patience in times of change.

_____ Exhibit consistency.

_____ Exhibit confidence, realizing that options, steps, and moves make things happen.

_____ Show empathy in interactions with others.

_____ Show openness, trust, and respect.

_____ Facilitate and motivate rather than direct.

_____ Believe in the human dignity of each person.

_____ **Total points**

Figure 5.1 An inventory for assessing your leadership qualities. (From Human Resource Management Associates. (1988). *Your leadership is showing.* Madeira, CA: Author.)

reduce formality. *This is not always easy to do!* For example, a person who has always been highly controlled emotionally is likely to find it difficult to conduct small talk or to deal with feelings.

When two people of opposite styles are in conflict, a considerable amount of "stretching" may be required in order to reach a solution. Since each perceives the other from his or her own framework, the experience can be like two people speaking to each other in different languages: they simply don't understand one another. This is why adaptability is such an important skill.

Here are some examples of leaders with limited adaptability, as described by other employees:

> My boss is like a chameleon. One day he's nice to everybody and the next day he yells at everyone.
>
> The way that I know the boss is normal is when he's shouting at people. That's when I know I'm doing a good job. It's when he's quiet that I get concerned.
>
> Our manager gets all upset if someone is three minutes late. Even though we all make up the time if we're late. But it's against the rules, and that's that.
>
> My boss is a controller. She controls everything and everybody. She makes all decisions, and then she delegates. But then she takes everything away from you.
>
> Our manager changes directions every time somebody thinks they have a good idea.
>
> Mine can never make a decision. He worries and frets about whether or not it's going to be right. Then he worries about if his boss will approve. Every time I raise a question or bring in an idea, he says, "I'll get back to you." But he never does.

In using the analogy that each of the four basic interaction styles involves a different language, we get a better idea of the importance of adaptability to productive relationships. *We tend to think that other people are like us and that they understand our language.*

Persons with limited adaptability:

1. Show limited adaptability to others' needs.
2. Tend to be specialists with well-defined interests.
3. Prefer certainty—"This is it."
4. Tend to stand on principle.
5. Emphasize position power.
6. Are consistent in their behavior—predictable.
7. Tend to be single-minded, purposeful.

Persons with high adaptability:

1. Show ability to adapt to meet the needs of others.
2. Tend to be generalists with broad interests.
3. Accept ambiguity—"Maybe."

4. Tend to be negotiable.
5. Emphasize personal power.
6. Are flexible in their behavior—unpredictable.
7. Tend to look at many sides of an issue.

Consistency and predictability are the strengths of those with low adaptability. However, a person of low adaptability tends to be rigid and has difficulty adapting to change. On the other hand, a person of too much adaptability may appear inconsistent or unbelievable.

The advantages of greater adaptability far outweigh the disadvantages. Adaptability increases our potential for meeting the needs of others, and thus establishing and maintaining productive relationships. It is important to note that adaptability is independent of interaction style. No single style is likely to be more or less versatile than another.

Skills That Aid Adaptability

Essentially there are three personal skill areas that enable one to "stretch" and better meet the needs of others: communication skills, style modification, and problem-solving ability.

Communication skills involve your ability to understand and speak the language of people with styles other than yours. To tailor communications to the needs of another is vital to productive relationships, and the key, of course, is your willingness and ability to listen. Your adaptability responds to the question, "What can I do to make it easier for that person to relate to me?" This also includes appropriate appearance, dress, mannerism, and speech.

Style modification is defined as temporarily adjusting your boldness and/or formality to encourage others to interact with you productively. This requires the ability to "stretch" your style in order to meet the needs and expectations of a person of another style.

Your *problem-solving ability* is determined by your willingness and skill at identifying options and alternatives. This includes your ability to involve others in the problem-solving process.

Suggestions for Developing Adaptability

People rarely make dramatic changes in their behavior. Some changes can and do take place, but they are gradual and several conditions must prevail:

1. You have to *really want to understand* how others see you.
2. You must *see a real need* to put the effort into developing more effectiveness in working with others.

3. You need to get a realistic picture of your interpersonal style and what you can do to improve effectiveness.
4. You must work at developing the ability to adjust appropriately to each situation.
5. While being true to your own style, you must learn how to reduce conflict in yourself and in others.

Lao Tsu said, "To lead people, walk behind them." In so doing you allow them to express their feelings. You can see dysfunctional reactions, and you can equip your followers with the tools they need to do the work and become leaders in their own right.

REFERENCES

Hersey, P., & Blanchard, K. (1982). *Management of organizational behavior.* Englewood Cliffs, NJ: Prentice Hall.

Karpman, S. B. (1968, April). Fairy tales and script drama analysis. *Transactional Analysis Bulletin, VII*(26), 39–43.

Kison, C. (1989, November). Leadership: How, who, and what. *Nursing Management, 20*(11), 72.

Oncken, W. Jr., & Weiss, D. L. (1974, November/December). Management time: Who's got the monkey? *Harvard Business Review,* pp. 75–80.

Pell, A. R. (1989, October). Selling your ideas. *Convention South,* 6(3) 1, 17, 24.

Walls, V. L. (1989, September). Culture building, people building and top performance. *Caring, VIII*(9), 13.

6

Coaching and Counseling

Bear Bryant was often heard saying that he was not a very good football coach but was a good coach of people. Coaching people is much more difficult than coaching a football team. You cannot place individuals in a certain spot without considering all that they are and feel. When policy meets personality and the two do not mesh, when personality conflicts occur amongst workers, and when anger and stress consume an individual, a coach will be needed. The coach's most important tool is not the whistle but counseling skills. Coaching and counseling go hand-in-hand; they are concerned with helping people be the best they can be in the workplace. The two skills foster healthiness by encouraging individuals to focus on taking care of themselves. As the coach or counselor, you want to help people discover how they handle conflict and what makes them feel good about who they are, without it being at the expense of other parties involved (Figure 6.1).

A discussion about coaching and counseling first requires an explanation of the dynamics of frustration, aggression, anger, and conflict.

Frustration breeds aggression, which is really a way of letting off steam. It can be manifested in three basic ways:

Handling Conflict on the Job

Avoiding
Avoid conflict when the issue is a low priority one or when it's just developing. Also, avoid conflict if someone else can handle the problem better.

Accommodating
Accommodate the person and the conflict when you want to build a relationship rather than win an organizational battle. Also, if you judge that the power dynamics are against you, cut your losses and endear yourself to the other party.

Competing
Compete in emergency-like situations when you must act with speed and decisiveness. Also, stay competitive when parties will not cooperate or would take advantage of your collaborative attitude. Use it to preserve organizational integrity or defend an unpopular decision.

Collaborating
Collaborate when your investment in the issue is high and you value the other person's viewpoint.

Compromising
Compromise when time to make a decision is running out and collaboration and competition have failed.

Figure 6.1. Handling conflict on the job. (From Pneuman, R. W., & Bruehl, M. E. *Managing conflict.* Englewood Cliffs, NJ: Prentice-Hall.)

1. In low-key reactions the attitude is: Something is bothering me, but not enough to make a big fuss about it. The focus is on the frustration and thus is impersonal.
2. In high-strung reactions the behavior indicates that the individual is truly upset because something very important is at stake. The frustration takes on a personal level and tends to focus on a person.
3. The attitude is: Let's just get the job done and not spend time analyzing it (Mali, 1981, p. 1080).

Aggression can lead to a display of anger. Anger is a reaction to a perceived external threat, but more importantly it is a choice, usually made at the subconscious level. Residing in the subconscious are backgrounds, attitudes, values, feelings, and perceptions all arranged, as we have previously discussed, into a pattern, a way of thinking. To deal with anger, the emotion must be extracted so that only the issues are put on the table. It is important to get anger out in the open because if it is not handled constructively, it can block communications, waste time, cause physical illness, lead to depression (which is anger turned inward), and fuel low morale in the workplace. On the other hand, anger has an energy about it that can be used to:

1. Move things away from dead center.
2. Motivate others to think.
3. Clear the air, because of its direct nature.
4. Communicate strong feelings and expectations.
5. Flush out misconceptions.
6. Indicate the readiness of an individual to move on to another step.

Anger demands attention because people do not get angry about things that they do not care about. The constructive options are quite limited: you can either confront the party that you are angry with or defuse the anger through venting, which is a way of buying time to cool off. Venting techniques include:

1. Laughing—humor provides an emotional release.
2. Thinking about how you would like to be treated if you were the other party, and acting accordingly.
3. Finding a healthy physical activity to burn off some of the energy.
4. Talking things out with someone you respect before you get to the point of boiling over.
5. Taking a mental vacation.

Confrontations can be risky. Conflicts often surface during the confrontational process, but this is not bad because the opportunity for greater understanding and dialogue is then available. Unresolved conflicts can build up and cause many problems in the future. When excessive conflict exists between two or more people, their behavior is rarely productive and they develop a strong need to discharge the conflict.

The leadership, management, and motivation of people really come down to the management of conflict. If there is too much conflict, there will be too few results, with the addition of inappropriate or defensive behavior. Knowledge about human behavior is an essential tool to help individuals successfully manage their level of conflict.

In order to be effective you must first:

1. Know your own style of interaction and how it affects others.
2. Be able to describe and predict the other person's needs from his or her behavior.
3. Develop skills to control the conflict that naturally occurs, so that it leads to a productive result.

There are four basic ways in which individuals handle conflicts:

1. "It's your fault, not mine."
2. "That's just the way things are."
3. "It's my fault, not yours."
4. "Let's deal with the problem, not who's at fault" (Mali, 1981, p. 1079).

The Thomas-Kilmann Conflict Mode Instrument (Figure 6.2), developed by Kenneth W. Thomas and Ralph H. Kilmann in 1974, can

---

Thomas-Kilmann Conflict Mode Instrument

1. a. There are times when I let others take responsibility for solving the problem.
   b. Rather than negotiate the things on which we disagree, I try to stress those things upon which we both agree.
2. a. I try to find a compromise solution.
   b. I attempt to deal with all of his and my concerns.
3. a. I am usually firm in pursuing my goals.
   b. I might try to soothe the other's feelings and preserve our relationship.
4. a. I try to find a compromise solution.
   b. I sometimes sacrifice my own wishes for the wishes of the other person.
5. a. I consistently seek the other's help in working out a solution.
   b. I try to do what is necessary to avoid useless tensions.
6. a. I try to avoid creating unpleasantness for myself.
   b. I try to win my position.
7. a. I try to postpone the issue until I have had some time to think it over.
   b. I give up some points in exchange for others.
8. a. I am usually firm in pursuing my goals.
   b. I attempt to get all concerns and issues immediately out in the open.
9. a. I feel that differences are not always worth worrying about.
   b. I make some effort to get my way.
10. a. I am firm in pursuing my goals.
    b. I try to find a compromise solution.
11. a. I attempt to get all concerns and issues immediately out in the open.
    b. I might try to soothe the other's feelings and preserve our relationship.
12. a. I sometimes avoid taking positions which would create controversy.
    b. I will let him have some of his positions if he lets me have some of mine.
13. a. I propose a middle ground.
    b. I press to get my points made.
14. a. I tell him my ideas and ask him for his.
    b. I try to show him the logic and benefits of my position.
15. a. I might try to soothe the other's feelings and preserve our relationship.
    b. I try to do what is necessary to avoid tensions.
16. a. I try not to hurt the other's feelings.
    b. I try to convince the other person of the merits of my position.

(Continued)

Figure 6.2 Thomas-Kilmann conflict mode instrument. (Thomas, K. W., & Kilmann, R. H. (1974). Copyright 1974, Xicom, Inc., Tuxedo, NY. Reproduced with permission. This material is intended for teaching purposes only.)

17. a. I am usually firm in pursuing my goals.
    b. I try to do what is necessary to avoid useless tensions.
18. a. If it makes the other person happy, I might let him maintain his views.
    b. I will let him have some of his positions if he lets me have some of mine.
19. a. I attempt to get all concerns and issues immediately out in the open.
    b. I try to postpone the issue until I have had some time to think it over.
20. a. I attempt to immediately work through our differences.
    b. I try to find a fair combination of gains and losses for both of us.
21. a. In approaching negotiations, I try to be considerate of the other person's wishes.
    b. I always lean toward a direct discussion of the problem.
22. a. I try to find a position that is intermediate between his and mine.
    b. I assert my wishes.
23. a. I am very often concerned with satisfying all our wishes.
    b. There are times when I let others take responsibility for solving the problem.
24. a. If the other's position seems very important to him, I would try to meet his wishes.
    b. I try to get him to settle for a compromise.
25. a. I try to show him the logic and benefits of my position.
    b. In approaching negotiations, I try to be considerate of the other person's wishes.
26. a. I propose a middle ground.
    b. I am nearly always concerned with satisfying all our wishes.
27. a. I sometimes avoid taking positions that would create controversy.
    b. If it makes the other person happy, I might let him maintain his views.
28. a. I am usually firm in pursuing my goals.
    b. I usually seek the other's help in working out a solution.
29. a. I propose a middle ground.
    b. I feel that differences are not always worth worrying about.
30. a. I try not to hurt the other's feelings.
    b. I always share the problem with the other person so that we can work it out.

Scoring the Thomas-Kilmann Conflict Mode Instrument

Circle the letters below which you circled on each item of the questionnaire.

	Competing (Forcing)	Collaborating (Problem Solving)	Compromising (Sharing)	Avoid (Withdrawal)	Accommodating (Smoothing)
1.				A	B
2.		B	A		
3.	A				B
4.			A		B
5.		A		B	
6.	B			A	
7.			B	A	
8.	A	B			
9.	B			A	

(Continued)

Figure 6.2 *(continued)*.

	Competing (Forcing)	Collaborating (Problem Solving)	Compromising (Sharing)	Avoid (Withdrawal)	Accommodating (Smoothing)
10.	A		B		
11.		A			B
12.			B	A	
13.	B		A		
14.	B	A			
15.				B	A
16.	B				A
17.	A			B	
18.			B		A
19.		A		B	
20.		A	B		
21.		B			A
22.	B		A		
23.		A		B	
24.			B		A
25.	A				B
26.		B	A		
27.				A	B
28.	A	B			
29.			A	B	
30.		B			A

Total number of items circled in each column:

—————   —————   —————   —————   —————

(Continued)

Figure 6.2 (*continued*).

be very useful in identifying how one handles conflict. It is easy and quick to complete. Simply choose the alternative that best describes you in a given situation, score the instrument by circling your answers and tallying them, then place the scores on a graph. The highest point indicates your primary style of handling conflict.

The Spiral of Disintegration

The spiral of disintegration is a graphic representation of the destruction of a relationship (or of an organization). Disintegration does not happen by accident. It is the result of a process that involves

Your Scores on the Thomas Kilman Conflict Mode Instrument

Instructions: Circle your score under each area, then connect these points with a continuous line. This will indicate your strengths and weaknesses

		Competing	Collab- orating	Compro- mising	Avoiding	Accom- modating
	100%					
		12		12	12	12
					11	11
High 25%		11	12	11	10	10
		10	11	10	9	9
	90%					8
		9	10			7
	80%	8		9	8	
			9			6
	70%	7		8		
	60%				7	
		6				
			8			5
Middle 50%	50%				7	6
	40%	5	7			
						4
	30%	4		6	5	
				5		
			6			
						3
	20%	3			4	
			5			
				4		
Low 25%	10%	2			3	
			4			
			3	3		
			2	2	2	2
		1	1	1	1	1
	0%	0	0	0	0	0

Figure 6.2 (*continued*).

people who do not have or who are not using people skills. This process may take a year or more to develop, or it could take place within a month. Ultimately, it will result in a disintegration of internal relationships. Interestingly, the spiral of disintegration can be reversed at almost any point, except of course, at the end (Rife, 1989).

Indicators:

    Distrust

    Hostility

    Polarization

    Rumors

    Blaming

    Power struggles

    Sabotage

    Withdrawal

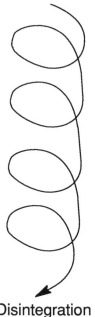

Disintegration

Back-up Behavior

Discharging Conflict Through Back-up Behavior

When people of the four basic interaction styles feel an intolerable amount of conflict, they tend to discharge this in a predictable manner. This "back-up" behavior accomplishes two things: it reduces conflict and it causes a deterioration in relationships. A key concept is that the person's ego has been hooked, and that person is no longer free to be uninvolved.

Back-up behavior, at its first level, is simply a natural extension of the person's level of boldness and degree of formality. In other words, a bold person gets more assertive and an informal person gets more emotional. Likewise, the easygoing person gets less assertive and the formal person exerts even more control over his or her emotions.

"Discharging" is a means of reducing conflict in the individual, and usually takes one of two basic forms: (a) a person will attempt to get away from the source of conflict or "flee," or (b) the person will act out the conflict or "fight." Thus, the discharge can occur by leaving the situation or problem altogether and refusing to face it, or by a spontaneous and usually demonstrative display of emotions that few others can understand. Because this discharge occurs when the person's normal style of behavior is not operating, it is often referred to as "back-up" behavior (Rife, 1989, pp. 8–6).

Types of Back-up Behavior

Results-oriented Behavior: Dictatorial

The results-oriented manager is typically impersonal, unemotional, and assertive. Thus the natural back-up for this style is dictatorial behavior. When frustrated, this type of manager often tries to take charge of the situation and the people within it, and to force things to come out the way that he or she wishes. This behavior will result in (a) *overcontrol* of the situation, and (b) some form of action. Under these circumstances it is best not to compete with the results-oriented person, but rather to direct his or her energies toward some additional achievements that you can support. Results-oriented people tend to respect others *who stand up to them or who confront*. This is particularly true if you make it clear to the manager that you are attempting to *achieve results* and *are not personalizing the situation* in order to make him or her look bad.

People-oriented Behavior: Attack

The typical style of the people-oriented manager is both emotional and assertive, thus the natural back-up behavior is to attack verbally. This attack can often be emotional, personal, angry, and even abusive. The most common expression is one of feelings about another person or an attack on the situation. When faced with this attack, it is best simply to listen without evaluation and without defending, and to *accept the emotion without getting involved or hooked by it.*

Security-oriented Behavior: Give In

Typically, the security-oriented manager is concerned about maintaining relationships and avoiding conflict. Thus, the back-up style is often to acquiesce or give in, which, of course, is a means of avoiding conflict and confrontation. This type of person will find that it is easier to go along with things rather than fight, and will also tend to get even. This behavior is designed to maintain a relationship regardless of cost. Giving in, however, can cause a loss of respect from results-oriented and people-oriented managers. When working with a security-oriented manager who is experiencing back-up behavior, it is best to *help him or her to find an area on which to focus.* It may be a task, or it may be an idea. It is essential for security-oriented persons to experience *appreciation*. They also *like to be asked for help.*

Task-oriented Behavior: Withdraw

The typical way for a task-oriented manager to relieve conflict is to avoid the situation or the relationship. This back-up behavior is a withdrawal from conflict. The withdrawal may become total in terms of both emotions and physical presence. This often occurs when the person is *confronted* or when his or her work is *criticized* by another person. *The least productive technique of working with a task-oriented manager in back-up behavior is to challenge or to insist on a response.* The most effective approach is not to deal with emotions and feelings, but rather to *deal with a process or procedure for moving ahead,* requesting help in deciding how to set up the process and gather data, and to take whatever steps are necessary to follow up on the situation.

Summary

All back-up behaviors are designed to reduce conflict. Unfortunately, they most often result in a deterioration of the relationship at the same time. People who are experiencing severe conflict over a prolonged period may resort to two or three progressive levels of back-up behavior (Rife, 1989, pp. 8.9–8.11).

By the time a person reaches the back-up level and has not yet relieved the conflict, there is a high probability of a distress reaction. It is also not unusual for the person to experience serious depression.

Dealing with Back-up Behavior

In dealing effectively with back-up behavior:

1. Recognize when conflict is becoming intolerable in yourself and in others.
2. Recognize when you or others are discharging conflict.
3. Identify and initiate options that will alleviate the conflict and have a productive effect.

On recognizing that another person is in back-up behavior, we have options: either pushing that person further into back-up or providing him or her with a way out. Unfortunately, when people's behavior is directed at us, it is usually easier *to push them further* than to *help them out.* This is a time when we need to step back from the situation, reevaluate, and determine our productive options.

Hostility

Hostility is one of the chief causes of depression, deterioration of relationships, and reduced productivity. Whereas back-up behavior is related to conflict, hostility is related to *self-respect*. When a person is made to feel intimidated, insecure, inadequate, or inferior, that person's self-respect is affected and the result is hostility. The discharge of hostility is often far more impactive than back-up behavior, and the person experiencing the hostility tends to have a more difficult time recovering.

As with the other forms of behavior, hostility can be recognized and controlled. Think about a recent time in which you experienced hostility toward another person or persons. You may have felt anger, antagonism, resentment, hurt feelings, inadequacy, or some degree of inferiority. You may have felt that another person's behavior was offensive or rude. Most likely you also felt some conflict.

Some effects of hostility are depression, inefficiency, loss of time, and impaired memory, concentration, and judgment. The more intense the source, the more intense the hostility.

Source ⟶ Hostility + Discharge

The three sources of hostility are intimidation, insecurity, and inferiority. Hostility results any time someone causes you to experience one of the sources (Rife, 1989, pp. 8.9–8.11). Hostility is easily generated in any interaction in which a person's *self-respect* is vulnerable.

Hostility may be *discharged* through any of the following behaviors:

Need to punish
Discrediting
Ignoring
Rejection
Belittling
Sabotage
Drinking/drugs
Withholding affection
Sarcasm
Rumor
Blaming

The sources of hostility vary with the interaction style.

Results-oriented Manager	**Security-oriented Manager**
Loss of control	Loss of security
Perception of being used	Too much change
Personal criticism	Lack of appreciation
Blockage of accomplishments	Conflict

People-oriented Manager	**Task-oriented Manager**
Loss of approval	Necessity for quick decisions
Personal rejection	Criticism of his or her work
Broken trust	Fast change
Isolation	Confrontation

Remember:

- Hostility is an automatic response when *self-respect* is reduced.
- You cannot rely on someone to whom you have been hostile.
- If you feel hostility toward a person, no matter how well he or she performs, you are not likely to appreciate or give credit to that person.
- Concealed hostility is always perceived by the other person. Thus we often *instigate hostility in others because of our own hostility.*
- *Blaming someone causes an intolerable drop in the other person's respect level, especially if done in front of others.*
- Sarcasm, put-down, and belittling or condescending comments are commonly used and are devastating forms of reducing the self-respect of others.

Since hostility is automatic when self-respect is reduced, the key to resolving hostile situations is *regaining a balance of self-respect.* What options do you have to restore this balance either in yourself or in the other person? (Rife, 1989, pp. 9.5–9.7).

People cannot be helped until they are ready! What you have to say is important, so getting them to listen is crucial. There are three times when you should never try to engage people in resolving conflicts: when they are tired, when they are angry, or when they have just made a mistake.

Timing is everything, so readiness must first be assessed. If the person is not ready, you may need to give him or her time to just be angry, to scream and shout or whatever is necessary to get ready. Next, encourage the subordinate to state how he or she sees things and why there is a problem: what is at the root of it and what would solve things. You want all the cards on the table. Now give your perspective as manager, and where there are misconceptions, wrong facts, and overlooked issues deal with them. One of your hardest jobs is to separate out what is personal and to focus on the problem. Start with things you agree on, but move to those you disagree on. Now let the subordinate come up with a plan for resolution that you both agree on, and how this will benefit him or her. There are reconcilable and irreconcilable differences. Look for a compromise in which both parties win on some of their points. If you reach a stalemate you may have to say this is the way it is going to be, and then impose your way (Mali, 1981, p. 1087).

We burn valuable energy on "my-way" or "your-way" efforts. To conserve strength for more important things, concentrate on what will work, not whose idea will prevail. Deal with specifics not generalities, never humiliate another individual, and avoid judging at all costs.

REFERENCES

Mali, P. *Management handbook: Operating guidelines, techniques and practices.* New York: Wiley.

Rife, L. G. (1989). *Organizational effectiveness through human engineering: A training program.* Unpublished seminar.

7

Personality Styles

Learning about yourself is one of the most exciting things life has to offer. The more you know about yourself, the greater will be your ability to shape events and to shape your relationships. How do you go about getting to know yourself? Study the conditions of life that are rich sources of information about your personality.

1. Observe the relationship between the onset of some emotional distress and provocation incidents in your milieu.
2. Observe circumstances that boost or lower your feelings about yourself.
3. Observe the form of your relationships with people.
4. Observe daydreams or night dreams.
5. Observe resistances to putting your insights into action (Wolberg & Kildahl, 1970, pp. 275–279).

In other words, pay attention!

Your personality is one of the things that distinguishes you from everyone else. Your habits, motives, values, feelings, and attitudes are all neatly wrapped in a package known as you. Personality is referred to as many things, but probably its most common synonym is one's "nature." The story is told of a scorpion who wanted to get across a body of water to reach the other side, but could not swim. It thought and thought about this dilemma, and then at last an idea: "I'll ride on the back of that turtle over there, who seems to be doing nothing at the moment." The scorpion asked the turtle for a ride, and without hesitancy the turtle agreed to help out, believing that the scorpion would not harm someone who was helping it. The scorpion climbed on the turtle's back, and they proceeded across the water. About half way across, the scorpion stung the turtle. With surprise on its face, the turtle asked, "Why did you sting me?" The scorpion replied, "Because it's my nature." Know your nature.

As a leader, you need to understand the nature of others and to separate nature from observed behaviors. Your job is not to alter anyone's nature but to capitalize on it so that observed behaviors and traits that will assist the goals of the organization can work without interference. How a person interprets things is important to know, for it is the key in helping that person find a workable, inner peace—and that is what you want in the workplace. Whether this interpretation is right or wrong is irrelevant. What is important is that an alternative is presented, which makes sense and can be owned and thus carried out.

Some authors, such as Drucker (cited in Bolton & Bolton, 1989), assert that supervisors should concern themselves only with observed behaviors and leave the rest to qualified professionals in this area:

> an employer has no business with a man's personality. Employment is a specific contract calling for specific performance, and for nothing else. Any attempt by an employer to go beyond this is usurpation. It is immoral as well as illegal intrusion of privacy. It is abuse of power. An employee owes performance and nothing else.[1]

Drucker's point is well taken, but I believe it is essential not to overlook the personality but to give it due consideration. People are not like dancers who put on a character's shoes for the performance and then take them off when the curtain falls. People carry their personalities with them all the time, and the more congruency there is between the individual's nature and the outer self, the more consistent people become and the more they are a joy to work with.

There are several building blocks of personality, according to Wolberg and Kildahl (1970, p. 39):

1. Heredity
2. Intrauterine and postnatal factors
3. The overall impact of the environment
4. The influence of mothering and fathering patterns

---

[1] From Bolton, R., & Bolton, D. G. (1989). *Social style/management style: Developing productive work relationships*. New York: American Management Associations. Reprinted by permission.

Reviewing these will be helpful in understanding yourself, but you may not have the chance to get such data on your subordinates. Consequently, you will need to find your own method for reading others. There are several ways to do this. Some individuals put people into animal categories and predict their behavior based on the nature of that animal. Others look to astrology or birth order. Others turn to personality tests such as the popular Myers-Briggs Type Indicator. This test was developed by a mother and daughter team, Katherine Briggs and Isabel Briggs Myers, based on Carl Jung's works. According to these authors we are either extroverts or introverts. Extroverts are considered outgoing personality types who enjoy people contact, while introverts prefer to keep to themselves. In addition, the authors classify people into sensors or intuitors, thinkers or feelers, judgers or perceptors (Figure 7.1). No one perfectly fits into these categories, but an individual's behavioral tendencies usually line up with one of 16 types based on combinations of these characteristics. Knowing the personality combination is like knowing the combination to a lock: it can open up the lines of communication and cut down on a lot of blow-torching.

Psychogeometrics

Dr. Susan Dellinger uses another method, known as psychogeometrics, to make some inferences. Preferences for a particular geometrical shape give clues to the subject's personality. Here is how it works. Subjects are asked to pick the shape they like best from five choices (Figure 7.2). Depending on their selection, you can get an idea of people's strengths and weaknesses, how to communicate effectively with them, and what motivates them. Below is a brief listing of traits, secrets to communication, and secrets to motivation attributed to each shape preference.

Traits

Square (Box)

Hard worker
Most organized and structured
Detail-oriented
Data collector
Has to know where everything is
Lover
Has do-it-yourself approach
Engages in long-term projects

Talking with Thinkers

- Be brief and concise
- Be logical and do not ramble
- List the pros and cons of each alternative
- Be intellectually critical and objective
- Be calm and reasonable
- Don't assume feelings are unimportant—they are just valued differently
- Present emotion and feelings as facts to be weighted in the decision

Talking with Sensors

- Be factual
- Document successful applications
- Reduce risk factors
- Thoroughly work out details in advance
- Show why it makes sense

Talking with Judgers

- Present a timetable and stick with it
- Don't surprise. Give warnings of coming changes
- Allow time to prepare
- Show that you also accomplish things and can be counted on to follow through
- Show your achievements, your results
- Take a stand, don't be wishy-washy

Talking with Feelers

- Get to know the person before getting down to business
- Be personable and friendly
- Demonstrate empathy by presenting areas of agreement first
- Show why the idea is valuable to people and how it will affect people
- Be aware of difficulty of accepting criticism
- Pay close attention to the way you are communicating—body language and nonverbals

Talking with Intuitors

- Give global scheme
- Don't let opportunity pass
- Use confidence and enthusiasm
- Indicate challenges
- Point out future benefits

Talking with Perceptors

- Allow for things to flow, not to follow calendar
- Bring in new information and ideas
- Allow for time for thorough discussion
- Allow for options
- Encourage autonomy
- Realize any change in direction is not necessarily impulsiveness

Figure 7.1 Rules for conversation with personality types. (Copyright by Jean M. Kummerou. Modified by Barbara C. Reynolds. From *The Tennessean*, January 7, 1990.)

Figure 7.2 Psychogeometrics test: The five geometrical shapes. (From Susan Dellinger.)

Not a strong team player
Procrastinates on major decisions—waits too long
Seen as indecisive
Needs to know rules and what is required
Likes forms
Needs to be specific—give information in writing
Complains about what is to be done
Likes pat on head—praise

Triangle

Leader
Loves recognition
Most ambitious
Moves up first—wants to be "number one"
Self-oriented
Skillful—can focus on goal
Clear thinker
Switches focus quickly
Always sure—sure person
Strongest of personalities
Dogmatic
Outspoken
Status- and title-oriented
Will decide for everybody
Decisive—wants own way
Likes to tell others what to do

Rectangle

Confused
Really boxed inside—sick of being in boxes
Wants to be triangle
Person in transition (growing, searching, changing)
Feels need for change
On daily basis, can be any of the other shapes

Unpredictable—Cannot determine how this person will act
Most open to new learning

Circle (Lovers)

Considers harmony most important
Wants everybody to be okay
Does not deal well with conflict
Does not like making unpopular decisions
Will blame self
Best communicator
Best listener
Feels what others are feeling
Reads people well
Motivator
Good in management—if others are allowed to make mistakes
Participative manager
Good where there are less lines of demarcation
Data collector about people
Has confidential information
Loves to solve problems
Glue that holds things together
Talks—wants everyone to agree

Squiggle (Sexual)

Keeps to him- or herself
Leaves early
Open-ended
Most right-brained
Most creative
Idea-oriented
Opposite of box
Sees the big picture
Thinks wholistically
Says "what if"
Interested in process and system—not small things
Not detail-oriented
Not a follow-up person
Good at start-up
Good motivator
Most excitable
Needs to be creative

Stifled by routine work
Needs variety
Good in sales
Does not like control/hierarchy
Unpredictable and hard to systematize
Requires lots of stimulation

Secrets to Communication

Square: ABCD—logical.
Triangle: Be specific—there is more than one solution.
Rectangle: Read the mood of the moment and then adapt.
Circle: Has to feel you are trustworthy—chitchat.
Squiggle: Quick and energetic.

Secrets to Motivation

Square

Details
Deadlines
Being organized
Private work area

Triangle

Authority
Secretary
Bonuses
Perks and status
Freedom to make decisions
Risk taking

Rectangle

Opportunity to learn and grow

Circle

Being needed
Harmonious organization
Time to be together

Squiggle

Room to move
Stimuli of all sorts

Newest equipment
Interesting people

Understanding personalities is really about the business of understanding the needs of others.

Understanding the Needs of Others

The psychological needs that are based on our interaction styles can easily come into conflict with the needs of another person of a different style. This usually results in conflict, and quite often the relationship deteriorates and/or becomes counterproductive. A person's psychological needs are also motivators. If you are to relate effectively with another person, that person's needs must be met, as well as your own. Sometimes you will have to meet that person's needs in order to have your needs met (Rife, 1989).

Individuals working in a climate in which none of their needs are met will spend most of their energy in a state of *survival,* and will have little energy left for being *productive.*

A person is motivated by his or her needs, *not by yours.* Consequently, the job of the human engineer is knowing which buttons to push. Using your knowledge on styles of interaction gives you a head start. Refreshing your memory can help you (Figure 7.3), then plan your strategy based on what you surmise.

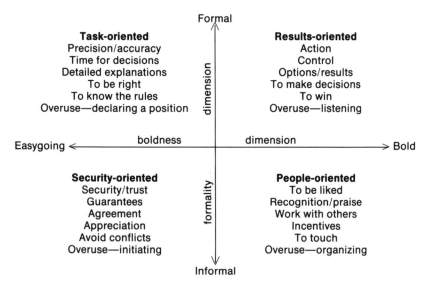

Figure 7.3   Style needs. (From Lou G. Rife.)

Working with Results-oriented Individuals

People who are results oriented tend to be less concerned about the needs of other people. Thus, they may appear to be independent, competitive, reserved, and even aloof in their relationships with others.

The results-oriented style characterizes a person who makes things happen. Such individuals may be assertive or even aggressive at moving toward goals. Unfortunately, they usually do not feel the need to express personal motives or feelings, and so their goals may not be identified by other people. They are interested in getting things done efficiently, and judge others by their own personal interaction style.

Though group decisions or meetings may be important within the organization, these individuals would prefer to work alone because they perceive other people as moving too slowly and interfering with their ability to get things done. They are often perceived as exercising power and control over their environment, in terms of both the people involved and the physical surroundings. However, they can appear very pleasant and warm, but usually on their own terms.

To work most effectively with results-oriented persons, your ideas can get the results that they are looking for. Discover objectives and goals, and find ways to support these and to assist with obtaining the desired results.

1. Don't waste time with small talk. Keep the relationship businesslike. It is not necessary to build a personal relationship unless that is obviously the desire of a particular individual.
2. Plan to ask questions about specific items. Stick to the "what," "why," or "when."
3. If you agree with the position of results-oriented persons, support the results desired rather than supporting them personally. Personal support is not important to them, but support of the ideas and objectives is. Indicate those things that you can do to achieve the objectives.
4. If you disagree with their position, disagree with the facts not with the person. Avoid personal criticism. Make your position clear based on facts and logic, and avoid emotions, feelings, and philosophy. Try to present options so that they can make the decision.

Working with People-oriented Individuals

People-oriented individuals tend to appear warm, to approach other people in an outgoing and animated way, and to be competitive.

They will involve you and other people in their thinking, feelings, and decision making, and like to work with groups of people. Persons of this style usually work fast and make fast decisions, and will often make impulsive decisions. They generally have a high consideration for the needs of other people, seek out social approval, and like to have a lot of "air time."

They want other people to take a personal interest in what they think and do. Personal recognition is important, and when there is high visibility, it is motivating. People-oriented persons respond to incentives, such as a special reduction in price, additional benefits, a special gift, etc. Too many facts or details often interfere with the process. Someone else will need to tend to this.

In working most effectively with people-oriented individuals, you need to make provisions for support of their ideas and intentions.

1. Take time for relating to them and for some socializing.
2. Look for their opinions and the things that they find most interesting, particularly in those areas in which you would like to develop a working relationship.
3. Plan to ask questions about their ideas and opinions, and take time to listen to what they have to say.
4. Spend some time exploring stimulating ideas, and also possible solutions, both from your point of view and from their point of view.
5. Don't deal with details, but put them in writing and summarize information.
6. Ask for their opinions and ideas about people.
7. If you agree, you should work out the specific details such as "who," "why," "what," and "how," since people-oriented individuals tend to disregard the "how to" and the detail work. *Your willingness to take the initiative to handle details will strengthen your relationship with the people-oriented individual.*
8. If you disagree, avoid arguing with people-oriented individuals; they feel a strong need to win an argument.

Working with Security-oriented Individuals

Of the four basic interaction styles, the security-oriented persons are the most relationship-oriented. These people work with and through other people in achieving results or influence, as opposed to directing things to happen. Their friendships and their close relationships are the highest priority. They tend to be the most loyal both to the organization and to their families; however, they also seek security and prefer to maintain the status quo. Security-oriented individuals show warmth and cooperation in getting things done, and usually seek the recommendation of others prior to making a decision. They are often slow to change and are low risk-takers, except in service to other people. They are the ones who will build teamwork within the organization and will also work toward reducing conflict between others. Belonging to a group is very important.

Because of the systematic and thorough approach to both task and people, individuals with security-oriented tendencies are often perceived by results-oriented and people-oriented individuals as too slow or wishy-washy in making decisions. This can cause frustration, especially when change is necessary. Yet these characteristics of thoroughness, dependability, and loyalty are often the factors that hold an organization together.

To work most effectively with security-oriented persons, you need to support their feelings and relationships with others and to show appreciation for what they do.

1. Spend time working with these people as individuals and time dealing with their personal situations, their families, and their interests.
2. Prepare your case in advance, and don't be disorganized or messy.
3. Establish a cooperative effort with them, and avoid overstating what you can realistically accomplish together to achieve the objective.
4. Communicate patience, and take time to listen to and include the personal goals of these individuals.

Working with Task-oriented Individuals

Persons of this style may appear uncommunicative, distant, and guarded in relationships. Task-oriented persons tend to judge others based on their own frame of reference, which is the need for perfection in their work. They are sensitive and worry about things being done properly. They are very accurate in their work and have a great need for knowing *exactly* how things are supposed to be done. Thus, they require *detailed explanations*, are usually slow to change, and tend to be low risk-takers.

Task-oriented persons make decisions and judgments based on facts, and will communicate these facts to others. They also separate *emotion* from *fact*, and often have difficulty understanding people who are unable to do this. They may even *distrust those who express emotion in business discussions.* The ability to apply reasoning and logic is one of their greatest strengths.

To work most effectively with these individuals, you need to show that you are capable of presenting a logical, factual, and accurate approach. The goal should be to show a great depth of knowledge and not to be too quick in seeking a solution.

1. Demonstration through action how you can help or how you can make a difference. The most effective approach is an organized, well-constructed, and well-documented presentation, which often needs to be in writing.
2. Task-oriented persons often expect others to oversell themselves or oversell what they can or will do. Therefore, be specific and yet be careful not to oversell.
3. Take your time and remain persistent. Be careful not to rush these individuals, even after you have established a relationship.
4. If you agree, look for possible areas of disagreement or dissatisfaction, yet be aware that agreement does not mean quick implementation. Task-oriented individuals seek assurance that the decisions are "right" and that there is no chance for error.
5. Don't offer *guarantees* or *commitments* that you cannot fulfill.
6. Define individual responsibilities clearly and in writing.
7. Present your case softly and nonthreateningly.

It has been said that employee personality clashes take up 9.2% of manager's time—or 4.6 weeks a year! Anything that takes up a month of your time is worthy of more than good intentions. It requires that you be *intentional* about putting together a committee, a team, a division. The key to walking on water is knowing where the stones are. You will know, if you spend some time studying personalities.

REFERENCES

Bolton, R., & Bolton, D. G. (1989). *Social style/management style: Developing productive work relationships* (pp. 15–16). New York: American Management Associations.

Rife, L. G. (1989). *Organizational effectiveness through human engineering: A training program.* Unpublished seminar.

Wolberg, L. R., & Kildahl, J. P. (1970). *The dynamics of personality* (pp. 275–279). New York: Grune & Stratton.

8

Handling Stress

Jesse Jackson wrote an article about the recent events in Washington, DC, involving Mayor Marion Barry. He highlighted a trait in Barry that he referred to as "the most elusive of all leadership qualities; grace under pressure" ("One Man's Lonely," 1990). I call this stressercizing. It is similar to aerobics—low-impact style: not necessarily something that you like to do, but you make it fun to do because you know you have to live with it and make it work for you. Often, it is not what you do but how you label it that makes the difference. According to Selye, stress is the nonspecific response of the body to any demand, whether it is caused by, or results in, pleasant or unpleasant conditions. He further describes it as not only "the spice of life" but life itself (cited in Adams, 1978).

Individuals trip the trigger of stress by the meanings they assign to the events taking place in their lives. In management, many of the perceived stressful events can be placed under a broad umbrella labeled "unresolved conflicts." Day-to-day management duties are full of never-ending sources of frustration and conflict. Some of these include:

- Unrealistic deadlines and timetables
- The dichotomy between how things ought to be and how they actually are
- Conflict vs. cooperation
- "I want it now" vs. restraints
- Integrity vs. self-advantage
- Avoidance vs. facing reality

- Self-direction vs. overdirection
- Commitment vs. noninvolvement (Applebaum, 1980).

In conjunction with the sources are one's perceptions of the degree of stress involved. Several factors have been identified that magnify the intensity of stress upon an individual.

1. The importance of the motives that are being blocked
2. How long the stress situation continues
3. The number of adjustive demands placed on the individual
4. The degree of familiarity with the problem
5. The strength of the opposing forces in the conflict
6. The spacing between where things are and the goal that has been set
7. The tolerance level of the individual for stress
8. The amount of control the individual feels he or she has over the events taking place (Applebaum, 1980).

Everyone is under stress. A certain amount is necessary; it causes the body to react with "fight or flight." In the work world you cannot do what comes naturally, so the body reactions work against you. The pent-up energy and emotions that for societal reasons cannot be released physically are turned inward. In other words, the body begins to fight itself, and all types of problems arise when one part of the body begins to argue with another. Body parts wear out more quickly, you age more quickly, and your resistance is lower, making you easy prey to disease. Many physical disorders are linked to stress, such as acne, colitis, ulcers, asthma, arthritis, headaches, heart disease, hypertension, and mental disorders.

Symptoms associated with job-related stress have a slightly different twist:

- Disregard for low- or high-priority tasks
- Reduced amount of time given to each task
- Change of boundaries to shift or avoid responsibility
- Blocking out new information
- Superficial involvement or appearance of giving up
- Negative attitude or cynicism
- Depersonalized or detached behaviors
- Going "by the book"
- Inappropriate humor
- Being overly precise
- Absenteeism

- Increase in medical claims
- Formal attempts to unionize (Adams, 1978).

As a manager, you are always on stage and thus observed. Your subordinates get their cues from you, and if you are being controlled by events rather than controlling them, your audience will know it. As a matter of fact, they too will feel tense and pressured.

Unknowingly, you could be asking your employees to meet unrealistic expectations, and the symptoms could be right before your eyes. Signals are usually given, so watch for them. An efficient leader is sensitive to changes in behavior in his or her employees and will be among the first to notice them. If the signs are present, the underlying causes should be flushed out. To quote James Baldwin, "Not everything that is faced can be changed; but nothing can be changed until it is faced."

Not having enough hours in the day to do all that is demanded of us can add to the problem. Take a close look at the word "deadline": the term was chosen deliberately—towing the line can kill you! Habits such as procrastinating, socializing, indecisiveness, and poor planning also eat up time, as do demands of the workplace such as phone interruptions, meetings, junk mail, equipment failures, and bureaucratic impactions better known as red tape. You cannot eliminate all of these, but grace under pressure requires that you manage your time wisely. To do so you must plan the events that make up your day and, to the best of your ability, control them. The elements that influence your control include your perception of time, knowing your time bandits, how and if you delegate, how you make decisions, and how you handle stress. Changing the method of your madness can make the difference between coping and crumbling.

First, get a grip on your own inner sense of time. Your perception of time is crucial. It is influenced by your management style, your culture, your sense of space, and what you value. Your individual tempo must also be placed in the context of others so that maximum effectiveness and the best use of time are achieved. Mary Ann Walsh Eells, an associate professor at the University of Maryland, has developed a test that many believe reflects an individual's sense of time (Figure 8.1). It is amazingly simple. Try it out. Take a sheet of paper, and draw three circles that depict your past, your present, and your future. Compare your diagram with those most commonly drawn, and read what the experts say about you and the sands of time (Tennessee Hospital Associations, 1979).

Different time orientations bring different expectations. When

Almost everyone draws a pattern of circles that falls clearly into one of eight common categories, though a few people blend two patterns together and thus exhibit some of the qualities found in both types. You should be able to match your circles with one or more of the following types:

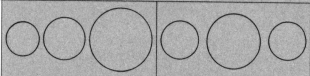

FUTURISTIC

About 65 percent of all people depict a steadily expanding sense of time. Such a person is in the mainstream of life, a solid and capable, if somewhat average, citizen. An association executive who draws a futuristic circle pattern probably does not worry unduly about past mistakes and injustices.

He is aware that he is living in the present and that today is important, but he nevertheless plans carefully for the future. He gets along well with almost everyone. He is less spectacular than some of this peers, but likely to compile a normal, if modest, career record. In short, he is probably a competent and conscientious worker, a steady asset to any association.

EXISTENTIAL

In many ways this person is the opposite of the Janus type. He is oriented toward people rather than objects. He is prompt and punctual. He will do well in all phases of the association business where human interaction is essential, but he may have difficulty coping with new technology.

The executive who draws the existential pattern lives most of his life in the present and may, therefore, experience difficulty visualizing long-term goals. The present is sometimes so overwhelming to him that, like the Janus type, he also exhibits a tendency toward alcohol abuse. In almost all other ways, however, Janus and existential types are so opposite that they may have interpersonal difficulties unless they are aware of their opposing ideologies.

JANUS

To this person, the present is unimportant, perhaps painful. He is a busy person but usually involved with things rather than people. An executive who draws this pattern is probably highly successful in organizing a smooth-running office, particularly in this age when technological innovations are omnipresent. He should, however, guard against a tendency to treat people with the same mechanical orientation.

He is optimistic about the future, intelligent, motivated, and decisive. He loves gadgets and typically will wear a digital watch featuring all the latest gimmicks, yet he is generally late for appointments. Because of his uneasiness with the present, however, the Janus type has a tendency toward alcohol abuse.

EXPLOSIVE

Charismatic and full of energy, this person does all of his living in the here and now. The association executive who draws the explosive pattern is probably a dynamo who is in constant motion, but the very speed of his actions may promote mistakes and difficulties in human relations. He talks incessantly but is often too busy to listen to others. He tends not to respect another person's space or time.

The explosive type may often seem to be successful because of the sheer force of his personality, but he is, quite literally, a time bomb. This impulsive, internally angry individual is a prime candidate for high blood pressure.

Figure 8.1. Time perceptions. (Reprinted with permission Walsh Eells, M. A. (1983, January). *Association Management*, pp. 58–59. Copyright 1983, American Society of Association Executives.)

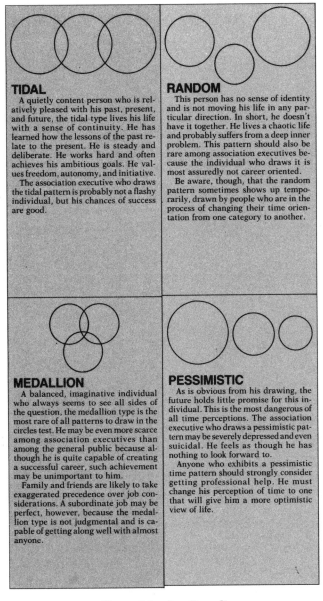

TIDAL

A quietly content person who is relatively pleased with his past, present, and future, the tidal type lives his life with a sense of continuity. He has learned how the lessons of the past relate to the present. He is steady and deliberate. He works hard and often achieves his ambitious goals. He values freedom, autonomy, and initiative.

The association executive who draws the tidal pattern is probably not a flashy individual, but his chances of success are good.

RANDOM

This person has no sense of identity and is not moving his life in any particular direction. In short, he doesn't have it together. He lives a chaotic life and probably suffers from a deep inner problem. This pattern should also be rare among association executives because the individual who draws it is most assuredly not career oriented.

Be aware, though, that the random pattern sometimes shows up temporarily, drawn by people who are in the process of changing their time orientation from one category to another.

MEDALLION

A balanced, imaginative individual who always seems to see all sides of the question, the medallion type is the most rare of all patterns to draw in the circles test. He may be even more scarce among association executives than among the general public because although he is quite capable of creating a successful career, such achievement may be unimportant to him.

Family and friends are likely to take exaggerated precedence over job considerations. A subordinate job may be perfect, however, because the medallion type is not judgmental and is capable of getting along well with almost anyone.

PESSIMISTIC

As is obvious from his drawing, the future holds little promise for this individual. This is the most dangerous of all time perceptions. The association executive who draws a pessimistic pattern may be severely depressed and even suicidal. He feels as though he has nothing to look forward to.

Anyone who exhibits a pessimistic time pattern should strongly consider getting professional help. He must change his perception of time to one that will give him a more optimistic view of life.

Figure 8.1. (*continued*).

those expectations are not met, the situation often becomes tense and, for some, stressful. This is the basis of unrealistic timetables.

Take a close look at your on-the-job time wasters and find solutions. The list of possibilities is exhaustive and more can always be included. To get started, look over Figure 8.2. Three of these time wasters need to be discussed in great detail: meetings, lack of delegation, and indecision.

On-the-job Time Wasters

Time Wasters	Possible Causes	Solutions
Lack of planning	Failure to see the benefit	Recognize that planning takes time but saves time in the end.
	Action orientation	Emphasize results, not activity.
	Success without it	Recognize that success is often in spite of, not because of, methods.
Lack of priorities	Lack of goals and objectives	Write down goals and objectives. Discuss priorities with subordinates.
Overcommitment	Broad interests	Say no.
	Confusion in priorities	Put first things first.
	Failure to set priorities	Develop a personal philosophy of time. Relate priorities to a schedule of events.
Management by crisis	Lack of planning	Apply the same solutions as for "Lack of planning."
	Unrealistic time estimates	Allow more time. Allow for interruptions.
	Problem orientation	Be opportunity-oriented.
	Reluctance of subordinates to break bad news	Encourage fast transmission of information as essential for timely corrective action.
Haste	Impatience with detail	Take time to get it right. Save the time of doing it over.
	Responding to the urgent	Distinguish between the urgent and the important.
	Lack of planning ahead	Take time to plan. It repays itself many times over.
	Attempting too much in too little time	Attempt less. Delegate more.
Paperwork and reading	Knowledge explosion	Read selectively. Learn speed reading.
	"Computeritis"	Manage computer data by exception.

(Continued)

Figure 8.2. List of time wasters, with possible causes and solutions. (From McConkey, D. D. (1974). *No nonsense delegation.* New York: Amacom.)

Time Wasters	Possible Causes	Solutions
	Failure to screen	Delegate reading to subordinates.
Routine and trivia	Lack of priorities	Set and concentrate on goals. Delegate nonessentials.
	Oversurveillance of subordinates	Delegate; then give subordinates their head. Look to results, not details or methods.
	Refusal to delegate; feeling of greater security dealing with operating detail	Recognize that without delegation it is impossible to get anything done through others.
Visitors	Enjoyment of socializing	Do it elsewhere. Meet visitors outside. Suggest lunch if necessary. Hold stand-up conferences.
	Inability to say no	Screen. Say no. Be unavailable. Modify the open-door policy.
Telephone	Lack of self-discipline Desire to be informed and involved	Screen and group calls. Be brief. Stay uninvolved with all but essentials. Manage by exception.
Meetings	Fear of responsibility for decisions Indecision	Make decisions without having meetings. Make decisions even when some facts are missing.
	Overcommunication	Discourage unnecessary meetings. Convene only those needed.
	Poor leadership	Use agendas. Stick to the subject. Prepare concise minutes as soon as possible.
Indecision	Lack of confidence in the facts Insistence on all the facts—paralysis of analysis	Improve fact-finding and validating procedures. Accept risks as inevitable. Decide without all facts.
	Fear of the consequences of a mistake	Delegate the right to be wrong. Use mistakes as a learning process.
	Lack of a rational decision-making process	Get facts, set goals, investigate alternatives and negative consequences, make the decision, and implement it.
Lack of delegation	Fear of subordinates' inadequacy	Train. Allow mistakes. Replace if necessary.
	Fear of subordinates' competence	Delegate fully. Give credit. Ensure corporate growth to maintain challenge.
	Work overload on subordinates	Balance the workload. Staff up. Reorder priorities.

Figure 8.2. (*continued*).

Meetings

Major events that many managers fail to plan adequately for are meetings. If one is in charge of the meeting, some prior planning does occur and centers around getting ready for the session. The anatomy of meetings requires that you not stop planning once the show begins. Successful meetings flow like a musical production. All events, including meetings, have an overture, prelude, performance, and cadence. One other thing: attendees of meetings also need to plan, even though they are not setting the agenda. No one should be allowed to squander your time.

Twenty-One Rules for Getting More from Meetings
Before

1. Explore alternatives to meeting.
   a. A decision by the responsible party often eliminates the need for group action.
   b. A conference call may substitute for getting together.
   c. Postpone the meeting. Consolidate the agenda with that of a later meeting.
   d. Cancel the meeting. Ask yourself, "Is this meeting necessary?"
   e. Send a representative. This gives a subordinate experience and saves your time.
2. Limit your attendance. Attend only for the time needed to make your contribution.
3. Keep the participants to a minimum. Only those needed should attend.
4. Choose an appropriate time. The necessary facts and people should be available. Schedule the meeting for before lunch, another engagement, or quitting time, if this is appropriate to the type of meeting being called.
5. Choose an appropriate place. Accessibility of location, availability of equipment, size of the room, and so forth, are all important.
6. Define the purpose clearly in your own mind before calling the meeting.
7. Distribute the agenda in advance. This helps the participants prepare—or at least forewarns them.
8. Compute the cost per minute of meeting by figuring the total salaries per minute, adding perhaps 35% for fringe costs. Assess the cost of starting late and of the time allocated to the topics on the agenda.

9. Time-limit the meeting and the agenda. Allocate a time to each subject proportional to its relative importance. Emotional topics should be placed at the end. This allows other items to be discussed and keeps the agenda from being dominated by one item.

During

10. Start on time. Give warning; then proceed. There is no substitute.
11. Assign time-keeping and minutes responsibilities. Keep posted on the time remaining and the amount behind schedule, if any.
12. Hold a stand-up meeting if appropriate. This speeds deliberations. Try it on drop-in visitors.
13. Start with and stick to the agenda. "We're here to . . ." "The purpose of this meeting is . . . ." "The next point to be decided is . . . ."
14. Control interruptions. Allow interruptions for emergencies only.
15. Accomplish your purpose. What was the specific purpose of the meeting—to analyze a problem, to generate creative alternatives, to arrive at a decision, to inform, to coordinate? Was it accomplished?
16. Restate conclusions and assignments to ensure agreement and to provide reinforcement or a reminder.
17. End on time. Adjourn the meeting as scheduled so that participants can manage their own time. Placing the most important items at the start of the agenda ensures that only the least important will be left unfinished.
18. Use a meeting evaluation checklist as an occasional spot check. Questions should be answered by each participant before leaving. Was the purpose of the meeting clear? Was the agenda received in advance? Were any materials essential for preparation also received in advance? Did the meeting start on time? If not, why not? Was the agenda followed adequately, or was the meeting allowed to wander from it unnecessarily? Was the purpose achieved? Were assignments and deadlines fixed where appropriate? Of the total meeting time, what percentage was not effectively utilized? Why? The evaluations, unsigned, should be collected for the chairperson's immediate review.

After

19. Expedite the preparation of the minutes. Concise minutes should be completed and distributed within 24 hours if possible, or 48 hours at the outside. If people can rely on receiving well-written minutes, those who really are not needed will be freed from

attending. Minutes are also a reminder and a useful follow-up tool, as shown in the next suggestion.

20. Ensure that progress reports are made and decisions executed. Provide follow-up to ensure the implementation of decisions and checks on progress where warranted. Uncompleted actions should be listed under "Unfinished Business" on the next meeting's agenda.
21. Make a committee inventory. Survey all committees, investigating whether their objectives have been achieved and if not, when they can be expected to be. Abolish those that have accomplished their intended purpose (Jenks and Kelly, 1989).

Delegation

Next, master the art of delegation. Delegation develops people, which is what an effective leader's agenda is all about. McConkey (1974) suggests that the following items lend themselves to being delegated:

1. Matters that keep repeating themselves
2. The minor decisions made most frequently
3. Details that take the biggest chunk of time
4. Parts of the job you are least qualified to handle
5. Job details you dislike doing
6. Parts of the job for which you are overspecialized

Always examine your reasons. Dumping busy work just to keep people busy or to make them the scapegoat is never a good reason for delegating. Avoid dictating methods, delegating half a task, hoarding information, and taking credit when the job is complete. All parties involved should agree on the outcomes and the time frame for completion.

Decision Making

Delegation and decision making go hand in hand. Most of your day involves either making decisions or communicating decisions made. When lack of decision making occurs, confusion, frustration, and anxiety are abundant. Indecisiveness points out a weak manager, a gofer for someone else, and an administrator of another person's dictates, or all three. Decisions cannot be made until the problems have been identified and the clutter cleared away. The exercise in Figure 8.3 illustrates the point. Follow the instructions and have fun.

Arithmetic Test

INSTRUCTIONS

In the Arithmetic Test, you will be given a series of 21 arithmetic problems, such as the following:

$5-3+8=$_____ $7+2-9=$_____ $6+1+3=$_____

All of the problems you will be given are at this level of difficulty. They are divided into 7 rows of 3 problems each. You are to write in the correct answer to all 21 problems as quickly as you can.

To make your task a little more difficult, the page on which the problems are presented has been filled with a lot of irrelevant material, such as pictures, words, and doodles. These have nothing to do with your task and have only been put there to distract you.

You will have only one minute in which to complete the test, so you will have to work quickly. When your time is up, stop your work.

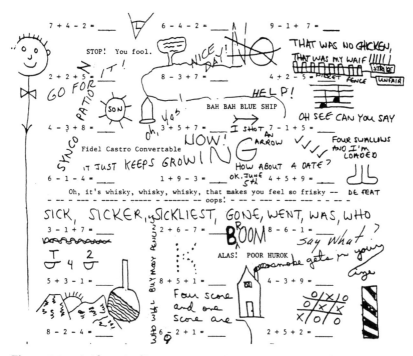

Figure 8.3. Arithmetic distraction test. (From Karp, S. A. (ed.). (1962). *Kit of selected distractions tests.* Brooklyn, NY: Cognitive Tests.)

How many problems did you answer? If you did all 24, that is exceptional. Most of us can only manage to do half of them because all the surrounding stuff is distracting. This exercise would be a breeze if the problems were circled first. The lesson is clear: isolate problems and deal with them.

Before you can do this, you must get to the underlying causes for poor decision making. The most common are:

1. Confused responsibility
2. Lack of authority
3. Inadequate data
4. Fear of making a mistake
5. Lack of defined target dates (Jenks & Kelly, 1989).

Once the cause has been identified and rectified, set the objective of the decision, determine possible solutions, evaluate each solution and select the best one for the organization, implement your plan, and then evaluate the results. If the results are not what you want, review the options you dismissed, look for new ones, develop a new plan, and implement it: if at first you don't succeed, try, try, try, again.

To help people get comfortable with decision making, create an environment for them to learn without pressure. Let them know that it is all right to be human and make mistakes. Reward those who do make decisions. Provide support in areas where they feel uncomfortable or lacking in knowledge.

Coping Mechanisms

Lack of decision making, meeting after meeting, lack of support, playing multiple roles, crisis, procrastination, unrealistic goals and expectations—these are the things that stress is made of. How well are you coping? Is your rubber band stretching with ease or about to snap? The coping quiz in Figure 8.4 could give you the answer.

Tension reliever's come in all shapes, forms, and fashions. Pick and choose from all categories, but do what works for you. Do not let situations steal your joy.

1. Use one calendar for all your time-related activities (The Franklin Institute, 1987).
2. Handle each piece of paper only once. The trash method could be of help here. Either toss it, refer it, act on it, sign it, or hold it for review or filing.
3. Listen to your own rhythm. Some people handle detail work better in the morning, for example.
4. Schedule phone calls for a certain time of day.
5. Be good to yourself each day. Do something for you.

Test Yourself: How Well Are You Coping With Tension?

How well are you coping with tension? Your answers to the following questions will tell you. Answer "YES," "NO," or "NOT SURE" to each question.

Coping Quiz

Yes	No	Not Sure	
☐ 1	☐ 5	☐ 3	1. Do you have trouble making decisions?
☐ 1	☐ 5	☐ 3	2. Do you dread meeting people or facing new situations?
☐ 1	☐ 5	☐ 3	3. Does "not going" or "not doing" hold an attraction for you in a way that it never did?
☐ 1	☐ 5	☐ 3	4. Do you find it hard to admit you're wrong?
☐ 1	☐ 5	☐ 3	5. Do you come unglued when you have several things to do?
☐ 1	☐ 5	☐ 3	6. Do you exaggerate your own importance and that of the things you have to do?
☐ 1	☐ 5	☐ 3	7. Do you constantly think of how pleasant it would be to escape for awhile?
☐ 1	☐ 5	☐ 3	8. Do you imagine that others are neglecting you?
☐ 1	☐ 5	☐ 3	9. Do you regard yourself as a failure?
☐ 1	☐ 5	☐ 3	10. Do you find it hard to get enough time away from your job?
☐ 1	☐ 5	☐ 3	11. Do you find yourself dropping old hobbies rather than taking up new ones?
☐ 1	☐ 5	☐ 3	12. Are you too critical?
☐ 1	☐ 5	☐ 3	13. Do life's simple pleasures fail to satisfy you?
☐ 1	☐ 5	☐ 3	14. Do your anxieties monopolize your thoughts?
☐ 1	☐ 5	☐ 3	15. Do small disappointments appear big to you?
☐ 1	☐ 5	☐ 3	16. Do people find you difficult?
☐ 1	☐ 5	☐ 3	17. Are you suspicious of the motives of others, even your family and close friends?
☐ 1	☐ 5	☐ 3	18. Are you plagued by self-doubt?
☐ 1	☐ 5	☐ 3	19. Are you keeping your anger and resentment bottled up?
☐ 1	☐ 5	☐ 3	20. Do you fail to get enough physical exercise?

———— ———— ———— = ———— **Total Points**

If your score is 75 or over, you cope with tension effectively. Good for you!
Between 50 and 75, you usually cope well, but there are times when tension gets you down. You need to be more aware of what can be done to overcome it.
Under 50, you are in need of help in coping with your tension and anxiety. Start dealing with one thing at a time. Tackle the most urgent thing first; then the rest will look easier. Find stress-reducing activities that work for you.

Figure 8.4. How well are you coping with tension? (From A Woman's Place. (1987, September/October). *Woman to woman newsletter.* Nashville, TN: Author.)

6. Do some relaxation exercises—this includes image rehearsing, meditation, aerobics.
7. Trust others. You cannot do it all.
8. Forgive and live. Carrying grudges and seeking vengeance use up valuable time and energy.
9. Learn to say no without feeling guilty.
10. Become a good listener.
11. Develop a sense for when to punch and when to punt.
12. Reserve the right to change your mind.
13. Cry if you feel the need to. Scientists have discovered that tears shed through sorrow or grief contain a morphinelike substance, so the body has a natural way to relieve itself (Evins, 1990).
14. Laugh at yourself and with others. A cheerful approach to life helps your immune system to gear up for a fight (Evins, 1990).
15. Compete with yourself and no one else.
16. Plan your day.
17. Take time to regenerate. Some of history's best teachers taught by example, and it would be wise for us to take note. Socrates and Jesus took breaks. They got away for periods of solitude and so should you.
18. Consider the wisdom of Lao Tsu:

Twenty-Two
Yield and overcome;
Bend and be straight;
Empty and be full;
Wear out and be new;
Have little and gain;
Have much and be confused.

Therefore wise men embrace the one
And set an example to all.
Not putting on a display,
They shine forth.
Not justifying themselves,
They are distinguished.
Not boasting,
They receive recognition.
Not bragging
They never falter.

Figure 8.5.

They do not quarrel,
So no one quarrels with them.
Therefore the ancients say, "Yield and overcome."
Be really whole,
And all things will come to you.[1]

Lao Tsu

REFERENCES

Adams, J. D. (1978). Improving stress management. *Social Change: Ideas and Applications, 8*(4), 1–11.

Applebaum, H. (1980). Managerial/organizational stress: Identification of factors and symptoms. *Health Care Management Review, 5*(1), 7–15.

Evins, N. (1990, January 28). Your sick body will get a good laugh out of this one. *The Sunday Tennessean,* p. 5G.

The Franklin Institute. (1987). *Focus on time management.* Workshop.

---

[1]From Lao Tsu. (1972). *Tao te ching* (G.-F. Feng & J. English, Trans.). New York: Random House. (Written in sixth century B.C.) Reprinted by permission.

Jenks, J., & Kelly, J. M. (1989). *Don't do, delegate.* New York: Franklin Watts.

McConkey, D. D. (1974). *No nonsense delegation.* New York: Amacom.

One man's lonely journey is significant for everyone. (1990, January 28). *The Tennessean*, p. 5-G.

Tennessee Hospital Association. (1979). *The Nurse Manager.*

9

Communication Styles

What do the following phrases have in common?

- You never get a chance to make a first impression.
- Actions speak louder than words.
- Read my lips!
- Can we talk?

They are all about communicating. They capture the various types of communication from the obvious to the subtle, and each has merit. Make no mistake, each type gets the message across. One cannot not communicate!

Researchers have concluded that:

1. The average white collar-worker spends 40% of his or her working day listening, but only comprehends 25% of the information efficiently (Hulbert, 1979).
2. Most people talk at a rate of approximately 125 words per minute (Hulbert, 1979).
3. Fifty to ninety percent of managers' time is spent communicating on an interpersonal level: 10% is spent communicating with their bosses, 40% with their subordinates, and 50% outside the chain of command, laterally and vertically throughout the organization (Mintxbert, 1973).
4. One-to-one interchanges need an average of four to six paraphrases for the participants to reach agreement on what is being said (Golde, 1979).

Being sure that you give and receive the intended message is essential. The communication transaction is not complete until the message is understood.

Individuals (and organizations) communicate because they want a specific response. If the response you are looking for does not occur, then you must ascertain before going any further that you have conveyed your message and it was understood but denied. Handling denials will be discussed later; brushing up on sending and receiving information is the primary aim here. Whether you have chosen to communicate by mouth, memo, policy, letter, or presentation, you must always take into consideration your audience. People have a wide range of thinking patterns, and your method should be diverse enough to encompass all of these. In other words, give whole-brain presentations (The Brain Company, 1989).

Discussions about the right brain and left brain are becoming more and more common. Whole-brain presentation means, in this case, adapting your messages for both left-brain and right-brain types, who have preferences for how they like to obtain information.

Left Brain	Right Brain
Reason	Faces
Logic	Patterns
Mathematics	Recognition
Language	Rhythm
Reading	Visuals
Writing	Creativity
Linear processing	Parallel processing
Analysis	Synthesis

The limbic system of the brain deals with emotions, and the cerebral system deals with data. Thus, your listener can be one of four types: cerebral left, cerebral right, limbic left, and limbic right. Putting this information into an action plan for implementing your presentation is not as complicated as it sounds. Figure 9.1 contains some suggestions for you to consider. If you take one idea from each quadrant as you prepare your communicating event, you may find that you are not repeating things quite as often.

Neurolinguistics is another useful area to refer to in fine-tuning your communication skills. This body of science deals with the way we store, access, and share information received by the brain. There

Planning a Whole-Brain Presentation

This worksheet provides a format for you to use in planning group presentations to ensure that you design your delivery for the wide range of thinking patterns that will be represented in your audience. Think about both the *content* that you include in your presentation and the *methods* you use to deliver the message.

UPPER LEFT	UPPER RIGHT
Content: • Key points/priority ideas • Summaries • Conceptual/analytical • Breaking down a problem into components • Quantitative Information **Methods:** • Concise, precise, efficient • Brief and orderly • Streamlined charts and graphs • Technical demonstrations	**Content:** • Conceptual/visionary • Options . . . possibilities . . . ideas • Future-oriented information • Change-oriented information • Posing open-ended questions **Methods:** • Drama • Metaphors/analogies • Verbal "pictures" • Graphics using images and artwork
LOWER LEFT	**LOWER RIGHT**
Content: • "How to's" descriptions • Implementation plan or progress • Procedures and policies • Details of events or process • Traditions, history, continuity of events **Methods:** • A, B, C, D walk-through of information • Chronological description • Step-by-step instructions • Well-organized graphics using numbers and words	**Content:** • People-oriented information • Morale/motivation issues • Inspirational content • "What impact on the people involved?" • Intuitive leaps/"gut feel" ideas **Methods:** • Color/music • Stories (people-focused) • Graphics using symbols and/or people • Expressive, emotional word choices

These are a few examples in each category. You will not be able to use all of these suggestions in each presentation, but try to pick at least one content and method from each quadrant. Come up with your own ideas for each quadrant as well.

Figure 9.1 Planning a whole brain presentation (© Ned Herrmann).

are three basic "modes": visual, auditory, and kinesthetic. Some people must see things, others must hear and process information, and others must touch, taste, and feel before they can incorporate the data. Everyone combines the modes, but each individual has a distinct preference. We give clues about our preferences by our word choices, and this is where listening, the other part of communicating, really becomes valuable (The Brain Company, 1989). Listen for the words used by the receiver. See which listing they fall under, and then tailor your word choices for maximum reception.

Mode Cues

Visual	Auditory	Kinesthetic
Eyeful	Amplify	Control
Bright	Call	Cool
Clear	Discuss	Emotional
Eye-to-eye	Earful	Fall apart
Foresee	Give audience to	Handle
Perspective	Hold your tongue	Drift
Pretty as a picture	Loud and clear	Grasp
Show-off	Silence	Hang
Vague	Tongue-tied	Lay my/your cards
Well-defined		on the table

As children many of us played the gossip game, in which a message is whispered into someone's ear and passed along from person to person until everyone in the room has been whispered a message. Usually, the last person receives a totally different message from the one initially whispered. Details are often dropped when things are not written down but passed on by word of mouth. Things should be put in writing, unless they are too personal and better said than read. Written communications are not something to dread. Most are too long and verbose. A guide often recommended for preparing written communications is the MADE formula (The Franklin Institute, 1987):

M = MESSAGE—give the bottom line.
A = ACTION—state what you want the receiver(s) to do.
D = DETAILS—state why and how.
E = EVIDENCE—attachments/enclosures.

Choose your words carefully. The wrong words can make something serious absolutely hilarious. They can be distracting and cause your message to be lost or overlooked. This list of announcements taken from church bulletins is a good example of how important it is to say what you mean:

1. This afternoon there will be a meeting in the south and north ends of the church. Children will be baptized at both ends.
2. Tuesday at 4:00 p.m. there will be an ice cream social. All ladies giving milk, please come early.
3. Wednesday, the Ladies Liturgy Society will meet. Mrs. Johnson will sing: "Put Me in My Little Bed," accompanied by the pastor.
4. Thursday at 5:00 p.m. there will be a meeting of the Little Mothers' Club. All those wishing to become little mothers, please meet the minister in his study.
5. This being Easter Sunday, we will ask Mrs. Johnson to come forward and lay an egg on the altar.
6. The service will close with "Little Drops of Water." One of the ladies will start quietly and the rest of the congregation will join in.
7. On Sunday a special collection will be taken to defray the expenses of the new carpet. All those wishing to do something on the new carpet, come forward and get a piece of paper.
8. The ladies of the church have cast off clothing of every kind and they may be seen in the church basement on Friday afternoon.
9. A bean supper will be held Saturday evening in the church basement. Music will follow.
10. The rosebud on the altar this morning is to announce the birth of David Alan Belser, the sin of Rev. and Mrs. Julius Belser.

As a rule, keep your message simple. Simplicity enhances understanding. Use the familiar word in place of the unfamiliar, the concrete word in place of the abstract, the short word instead of the long one, and the single word in place of a round-about phrase (Tennessee Hospital Association, 1978).

Saying no is something most of us find difficult to do. Refusing requests is part of your job, and putting this off makes matters worse. It has to be done from time to time, and there are a few things you can do to make things go more smoothly. First, remember that you are rejecting the request not the individual. Make sure you understand what is being asked and why. If appropriate, give your reasons for the denial. Empathizing with the originator of the request is acceptable, but being overly apologetic defeats your purpose. Allow the other person to save face, and end the conversation on a positive note.

Reprimanding people is another managerial task. It should be done to obtain a change in attitude and/or behavior, never to humiliate, degrade, or punish. Before the process begins, make sure you have the facts. If there is a shadow of a doubt about anything, throw it out. Nothing is more destructive to a relationship than false accusations. Be clear and concise, and talk in a straightforward fashion. Give the nature and extent of the reprimand. Assure the individual that there are no grudges on your part. Above all be fair. Use "I" messages— these are less threatening and help you state your point of view rather than passing judgment. Address behaviors or actions and describe situations. Listen, with more than your ears. Use your eyes, intuitiveness, and anything else that gives you feedback about the other person's receptivity. Clear up misunderstandings, and schedule follow-ups if necessary.

In communicating, analyze the audience and develop the message. Keep in mind the date the information is needed, the cost for the communication event, what needs emphasis or reinforcement, the best method for getting things across, and most importantly, the purpose.

> Avenues of communication are as integral to a management structure as various types of leadership, styles and trainings used to make superiors aware of management principles because "frank and open communications can minimize suspicions, correct misunderstandings, and build teamwork." (Jones et al, 1990)

Two tools that can lead to clear avenues of communication are Johari's window (Figure 9.2) and assertiveness skills. Two psychologists, Joseph Luft and Harry Ingram, developed a model that shows how trust and mutual respect can be enhanced through the process of feedback and self-disclosure. Johari's window is a representation of self as perceived by the individual and by others. As the level of openness and trust changes, more about an individual is shared, creating an "open window" with no hidden agendas (Mali, 1981).

Basketball games have rules and referees to keep the game respectable and fair. If someone fouls you, the referee is there to call it—to stop the game for a moment and give you a chance at a fair shot. Life is not that way. You might get jabbed in the eye, elbowed, kneed, or knocked down, and in many instances you are screaming foul but it seems that no one is hearing you, cares, or will blow the whistle and say, "Enough of this, time out." So what is a person in this situation to do? Speak up. It is not what you say but how you say it. The story is told of a teacher who walked into a noisy classroom, slapped her hand on the desk, and ordered sharply, "I demand a little pandemo-

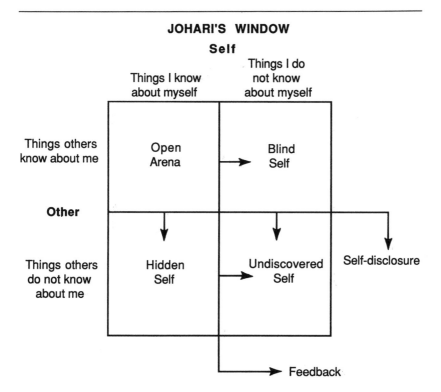

JOHARI'S WINDOW

The Open Arena is the windowpane, which is composed of what an individual and others know about a person. This includes public behavior and is characterized by open exchange of information. Improved communication results from enlarging the Open Arena. This is achieved by reducing (1) the Blind Self, which contains what persons do not know about themselves but what others know, and (2) the Hidden Self, which contains information persons know about themselves but which they choose not to reveal to others. The Undiscovered Self contains areas that neither the person nor others know about an individual; it is the unconscious part of the self. This material lies beneath the surface; however, through exchange of information, this material has a potential for becoming known both to the public and to the individual.

Figure 9.2 Johari's window. (Adapted from Fisher, D. W. (1982). A model for better communication. *Supervisory Management, 31,* 25–26. By permission of the publisher. Copyright 1982, American Management Association, New York. All rights reserved.)

nium.'' The class quieted down immediately. ''It isn't what you ask for,'' she announced later in the teacher's lounge. ''It's how you ask for it.''

Assertiveness is about expressing your needs and goals, and communicating in a way that is open and honest. First, assertive individuals realize that there is nothing wrong with them. They just want to be themselves and let others do the same. So if friction occurs at the point where two selves meet, it is not personal—just a "chemical" reaction. Second, others will not know how you feel unless you tell them. Third, continue to do what is right and treat others as you wish to be treated. You cannot control their behavior. You can control your own, and it all begins with a thought. Negative thinking can make you resentful, ill, depressed, and cynical. It can cause you to strike out at things that mean you no harm. Rollo May (1972) says that assertiveness is a component of power, and he sees it as a part of a continuum (Figure 9.3). The list of techniques for learning assertiveness is almost endless. Psyche, Inc., at the University of Minnesota, suggests the following techniques and guidelines:

Do You Assert Yourself?

Nonassertive Individual	Assertive Individual	Aggressive Individual
Avoids problem	Faces problem	Attacks person instead of dealing with problem
Allows manipulation by others	Lets others know what he or she thinks and feels and gains their respect	Takes advantage of others; others fear and avoid him or her
Gives up rights	Claims rights	Considers own rights superior to those of others
Lets others choose activities	Makes own choices	Chooses activities for others
Hopes goals will be accomplished	Expresses goals and works toward them	Works toward goals
Lacks confidence	Possesses self-confidence	Exhibits demanding, hostile, egotistical behavior
Develops a pattern of self-denial; feels inadequate to express thoughts and feelings; unable to achieve goals	Thinks and behaves in ways that coincide with his or her rights; often able to achieve goals	Behaves verbally or physically in a way that expresses own rights, but at the expense of others

Figure 9.3   Do you assert yourself? (Adapted from YOUR PERFECT RIGHT (Second Edition) © 1974 by Robert E. Alberti and Michael L. Emmons. Reproduced by permission of Impact Publishers, Inc., P.O. Box 1094, San Luis Obispo, CA 93406. Further reproduction prohibited.)

1. Know and express your beliefs and rights. Examples: "I have the right to disagree." "I have the right to have my opinions given respect." "I have the right to be myself."
2. Reinforce your identity as a person by expressing your thoughts and feelings directly. Refer to "I," and use action verbs or behavioral terms. Examples: "I feel . . ." "I want . . ." "I find . . ." "Doing . . . is fine with me."
3. Avoid general, impersonal statements (using you, we, it). Examples: "We all know . . ." "You can't expect . . ." "Isn't it true about this case that . . ."
4. In a group, make direct comments to specific persons rather than to the group in general.
5. Say "I *won't* do . . ." rather than "I *can't* . . ." The latter implies lack of power or ability to do something. The former says the person is assuming responsibility for his or her statements.
6. Be aware of assertive nonverbal behavior—standing with both feet firmly planted and using abdominal breathing.
7. Use assertive statements:
   - *Simple assertive* (letting the other person know what you feel and think): An example of this would be to say, "I would like to see . . ." "I think . . ."
   - *Empathic assertive* (acknowledging the other person's needs): "I know that you are very busy, but I want to tell you . . ." "I know how much you like to do this, but I feel that . . ."
   - *Confrontive assertive* (calling someone's attention to something): "You said you would write that report, but you haven't."
   - *Soft assertive* (expressing your appreciation to another person): "I sure did appreciate it when you did this for me."
   - *Persuasive assertive* (letting the other person know where you agree and disagree and how you feel things should proceed): "I agree with most of what you say, but I also feel . . ." "I feel you have some good ideas, but I see other . . ."
8. Use certain techniques when someone gives you a "pull-down." To buy time:
   - "I need a few minutes to think about what you're saying."
   - Use silence.
   - "It seems to me . . ." (State your feelings clearly without "beating around the bush.") (Bakdash, 1978).

Assertiveness leads to self-confidence, which ultimately leads to increased self-esteem—and success is sure to follow. Assertiveness commands rather than demands respect. It does not require rudeness, a loud voice, or the use of threats. It allows your humanness to come through. It is affirming of both your self-worth and that of others.

REFERENCES

Bakdash, D. P. (1978, October). Becoming an assertive nurse. *American Journal of Nursing*, pp. 1711–1712.

The Brain Company. (1989, April). *The brain workshop.* Burlington, MA: Author.

The Franklin Institute. (1987). *Focus on time management.* Seminar.

Golde, R. A. (1979). *What you say is what you get* (p. 16). New York: Hawthorne Books.

Hulbert, J. (1979, February). They won't hear you, if you don't listen. *Administrative Management*, pp. 56–62.

Jones, M. A., et al. (1990). A paradigm for effective resolution of interpersonal conflict. *Nursing Management, 21*(2), 64J.

Mali, P. (1981). *Management handbook: Operating guidelines, techniques, and practice* (pp. 1459–1460). New York: Wiley.

May, R. (1972). *Power and innocence* (pp. 121–179). New York: W. W. Norton.

Mintxbert, H. (1973). *The nature of managerial work* (p. 25). New York: Harper & Row.

Tennessee Hospital Association. (1978). *What an executive should know about communicating effectively.* Nashville: Author.

10

Timeless Lessons

On looking over the first nine chapters of this book, I realized that there was so much more I wanted to share and yet had left unsaid. Many of these thoughts are unrelated as subjects in and of themselves, but they do have a common denominator—your style. They can shape it, affect it, and characterize it.

The way you do things is as important as what you do, and perhaps more so. A style that values the individual and struggles to understand rather than change others, creating an environment where policy meets personality, amicably and harmoniously, is as good as it gets.

Keeping a journal, like leadership, is a spiritual endeavor. It is a wonderful way of storing a collection of your thoughts and watching yourself grapple with what I call tough realities and problems. If you keep a journal regularly, you will find among your written pages stories, quotes, poems, and statements that mean something to you and boost your immune system at the same time. Here are a few from my personal collection. Reviewing these thoughts, extracts, and rubrics periodically helps me to keep my perspective. Most of all, they encompass the things I left unsaid.

RUBRIC I

How Do You Cook an Elephant? One Piece at a Time.

Many of the tasks on your "to do" list will seem overwhelming at first glance—and at the second and third glance! This realization can cause mental paralysis and leave you with a feeling of inadequacy. This does not have to be. Break your tasks into manageable parts, rename your problems, do the best you can for one day, and leave the rest for tomorrow. Follow the advice in "Just for Today" by Sibyl F. Partridge:

Just For Today

1. Just for today I will be happy. This assumes that what Abraham Lincoln said is true, that "most folks are about as happy as they make up their minds to be." Happiness is from within; it is not a matter of externals.
2. Just for today I will try to adjust myself to what is, and not try to adjust everything to my own desires. I will take my family, my business, and my luck as they come and fit myself to them.
3. Just for today I will take care of my body, I will exercise it, care for it, nourish it, not abuse it nor neglect it, so that I will be a perfect machine for my bidding.
4. Just for today I will try to strengthen my mind. I will learn something useful. I will not be a mental loafer. I will read something that requires effort, thought and concentration.
5. Just for today I will exercise my soul in three ways; I will do somebody a good turn and not get found out. I will do at least two things I don't want to do, as William James suggests, just for exercise.

6. Just for today I will be agreeable. I will look as well as I can, dress as becomingly as possible, talk low, act courteously, be liberal with praise, criticize not at all, nor find fault with anything and not try to regulate nor improve anyone.
7. Just for today I will try to live through this day only, not to tackle my whole life problem at once. I can do things for twelve hours that would appall me if I had to keep them up for a lifetime.
8. Just for today I will have a program. I will write down what I expect to do every hour. I may not follow it exactly, But I will have it. It will eliminate two pests, hurry and indecision.
9. Just for today I will have a quiet half-hour all by myself and relax. In this half-hour sometimes I will think of God, so as to get a little more perspective into my life.
10. Just for today I will be unafraid, especially I will not be afraid to be happy, to enjoy what is beautiful, to love, and to believe that those I love, love me.[1]

RUBRIC II

Remember Everybody Is Somebody's Child.

Somebody's Child

Don't be too quick to condemn me,
Because I have made a bad start;
Remember you see but the surface,
And know not what's in the heart.
I may bear the marks of a sinful life,

---

[1]From Carnegie, D. (1984). *How to stop worrying and start living* (p. 100). New York: Simon & Schuster. Reprinted by permission.

And I may have been a bit wild;
But back of all remains this fact,
That I am somebody's child.
My cheeks by tears may be polished,
And my heart is no stranger to pain;
I know what it is to be friendless,
and to learn each affliction means gain.
I may be out in life's storm,
And misfortune around me has piled;
But kindly remember this little fact,
That I am somebody's child.
Probably to-night you'll be happy
In some joys or pleasures you'll share:
And that very same moment may find me,
Tearfully pleading in prayer.
So don't be too harsh when you judge me,
For your judgment with God will be filed;
You would know—could you see past surface—
That I am somebody's child.[2]

Charles P. Wilson

Abraham Lincoln espoused the philosophy that "all of us are the children of condition, of circumstances, of environment, of education, of acquired habits and of heredity." If you had inherited the same set of conditions as those whom you find intolerable, perhaps you would be like them. Therefore, look beyond the bad for something good.

Charles Wilson's poem reminds us that everybody is valuable as a person and therefore worthy of being treated with respect, even when behaving in ways that are hard to tolerate. It says that we all have good days and bad ones. It says that not all of us will have MBAs and attaché cases. It asks that we not be quick to judge and even quicker to get even. It asks that we not personalize our displeasures and that we hate the situation not the person. You would not want your child mistreated, so don't mistreat someone else's.

---

[2]From Wilson, C. P. (1935). Somebody's child. In R.T. Kerlin (Ed.), *Negro poets and their poems* (3rd ed.) Washington, DC: Associated Publishers. Reprinted by permission.

RUBRIC III

Polices That Encourage Lying Are of No Good to Anyone.

The burning of fossil fuels is ruining our environment and making it hotter and hotter. And in today's work world, fossilized ideas such as old worn-out decisions, useless policies, and management styles that ignore individual needs and use threats to get people to comply, are causing corporate America to heat up. Policies should serve as guidelines, not prison bars or barbed-wire fences. They should not be used as walls to hide behind, or as a means of punishment or self-aggrandizement. If policies encourage lying or give energy to the development of ways to beat the system, they are probably worthless as written. Go back to the drawing board and start over. Your goal should be to save time, not squander it.

We must reverse the trends by finding alternative sources of energy—natural resources such as self-love, self-esteem, and trusting others.

RUBRIC IV

Be Human.

Bo Jackson is one of this nation's most outstanding athletes. As the commercials poignantly say: "Bo knows football. Bo knows baseball. Bo knows basketball—but Bo doesn't know diddley," if he doesn't know about the human condition and accept the fact that he too is human.

Being human means that you will make mistakes and make bad calls on occasion. It means that you will not and should not expect to know everything there is to know about every subject that you will come into contact with.

It demands that you find the courage from within to say what Mark McCormack feels are the three hardest things for people to say:

> I don't know.
> I need help.
> I was wrong.[3]

There is one more three-word sentence you should practice saying until it is second nature:

> I am sorry.

None of these phrases will cost you anything. They will enhance your value and effectiveness.

RUBRIC V

Nothing Is More Powerful Than a Made-up Mind!

---

[3]From McCormack, M.H. (1984). *What they don't teach you at Harvard Business School* (pp. 69–71). New York: Bantam Books.

The *Wizard of Oz* is a wonderful story for a variety of reasons. One of its recurring themes is "follow the yellow brick road." Dorothy, the Tin Woodman, the Cowardly Lion, and the Scarecrow all had the same goal—to see the Wizard, and they all knew which route to take. They focused and kept their distractions from defeating them. They were determined.

Manage your disappointments. Seek to understand the pain you are experiencing. Pain is universal. It is a signal that growth and learning are about to occur. Apply the new knowledge. View failures as delays not denials. Focus on things and conditions you can do something about. Give them your undivided attention. Albert Einstein was inadequate in mathematics. Henry Ford went broke. Walt Disney went bankrupt seven times! These men never lost sight of their goals, and neither should you.

Set your goals and let no one keep you from obtaining them.

Stick To Your Job

Diamonds are only chunks of coal
That stuck to their jobs, you see.
If they'd petered out like most of us do,
Where would the diamonds be?
It isn't the fact of making a start.
It's the sticking that counts, I'll say.
It's the fellow who knows not the meaning of fail,
But hammers and hammers away.
Whenever you think you have come to the end
And you're beaten as bad as can be;
Remember that diamonds are chunks of coal
That stuck to their jobs, you see.[4]

Minnie Richard Smith

Songs such as Billy Ocean's "When the Going Gets Tough, the Tough Get Going" and Bobby McFerrin's "Don't Worry, Be Happy" were written to help you get through bad times. We all have down times, and the act of looking down is a part of these times. Research has shown that looking down gives one a sense of fatigue and depression. It makes the load you carry seem psychologically heavier.

Looking up allows you to see the sky with its limitless boundaries.

---

[4]From Smith, M. R. (1990, March 13). *President's message*. Nashville: Tennessee Hospital Association. Reprinted by permission.

RUBRIC VI

When You're Feeling Down, Look Up.

It shows you how clouds drift into the picture for a while and then are blown on by the wind. It fosters a sense of hope. The sun's rays peeping through the clouds tell you to look beyond the bad for something good. Accept the ordinaries of life. Stop thinking that your problems are worse than, more severe than, or different from other people's problems.

You can give up or go on. The day is yours. It is up to you.

RUBRIC VII

Answers Come from the Most Unexpected Places.

Years and years ago, a truck with a load of fuel cargo became wedged between an overpass and the road on which it traveled. Emergency workers were summoned to develop a strategy for getting the truck unstuck without damaging the overpass. Traffic was blocked in both directions, and people were trapped in their cars for hours. As the crowd became more restless, so did the workers and truck driver. It was difficult to think clearly, and the only solution seem to be a destructive one—tear up the overpass. Just as a bulldozer was called in, a small boy on his way home from a baseball game arrived on the scene. "Hey mister," he screamed, "what's going on here?" He was told that the truck was stuck and that he should get out of the way before he got hurt. The boy raised his cap, bent down and looked underneath the truck, scratched his head, and then tugged the head-crewman's shirt sleeve. "Why don't you let the air out of the truck's tires? That should make enough room for the truck to clear?" In amazement the crewman said "Son, that's a great idea. Thanks!"

Don't rule out any suggestions for solving a problem. The way people look, their educational or cultural backgrounds, or their age, should not be the criteria for deciding whether what they have to say is worthwhile. They just might have the solution you seek.

RUBRIC VIII

Integrity Is to Excellence What Carbon Is to Steel.

Integrity deals with the wholeness of things. It does not refer to the individual nature of things but rather to their completeness. This wholeness means that all multidimensional approaches are applied to all decisions, tasks, and goals so that the needs of all parties involved are considered. Once those who make up the organization realize that the leader is looking out for them above all else, the organizational leeches known as conceit, cynicism, hate, jealousy, self-pity, egotism, greed, and humiliation have no breeding ground and no host upon which to fix themselves. They starve from lack of nourishment and perish.

Ouchi says its better in *Theory Z*:

Perhaps the single most notable characteristic among those who have succeeded at going from A to Z has been an almost palpable character of integrity. By integrity I do not mean preaching morality to others; I mean an integrated response to problems, an integrated and consistent response to customers and employees, to superiors and subordinates, to problems in finance and in manufacturing. A person of integrity treats secretaries and executives with equal respect and approaches subordinates with the same understanding and values that characterize his family relationship. A person with integrity can be counted upon to behave consistently, even as organizational conditions change such a person can be trusted and can provide that key human capital from which others can draw in the process of change.[5]

People of integrity can be counted on. Their views are not myopic and their concerns are guided, not driven, by the mechanisms that keep organizations intact.

Excellent leaders are leaders with integrity.

RUBRIC IX

Delays Are Not Denials.

I Stood Yesterday. I Can Stand Today

I have been through the depths of poverty and sickness. When people ask me what has kept me going through the troubles that come to all of us, I always reply: "I stood yesterday. I can stand today. And I will not permit myself to think about what *might* happen tomorrow."

I have known want and struggle and anxiety and despair. I

---

[5]From Ouchi, W. G. (1981). *Theory Z: How American business can meet the Japanese challenge* (p. 101). Reading, MA: Addison-Wesley. Reprinted by permission.

have always had to work beyond the limit of my strength. As I look back upon my life, I see it as a battlefield strewn with the wrecks of dead dreams and broken hopes and shattered illusions—a battle in which I always fought with the odds tremendously against me, and which has left me scarred and bruised and maimed and old before my time.

Yet I have no pity for myself; no tears to shed over the past and gone sorrows; no envy for the women who have been spared all I have gone through. For I have lived. They only existed. I have drunk the cup of life down to its very dregs. They have only sipped the bubbles on top of it. I know things they will never know. I see things to which they are blind. It is only the women whose eyes have been washed clear with tears who get the broad vision that makes them little sisters to all the world.

I have learned in the great University of Hard Knocks a philosophy that no woman who has had an easy life ever acquires. I have learned to live each day as it comes and not to borrow trouble by dreading the morrow. It is the dark menace of the picture that makes cowards of us. I put that dread from me because experience has taught me that when the time comes that I so fear, the strength and wisdom to meet it will be given me. Little annoyances no longer have the power to affect me. After you have seen your whole edifice of happiness topple and crash in ruins about you, it never matters to you again that a servant forgets to put the doilies under the finger bowls, or the cook spills the soup.

I have learned not to expect too much of people, and so I can still get happiness out of the friend who isn't quite true to me or the acquaintance who gossips. Above all, I have acquired a sense of humor, because there were so many things over which I had either to cry or laugh. And when a woman can joke over her troubles instead of having hysterics, nothing can ever hurt her much again. I do not regret the hardships I have known, because through them I have touched life at every point I have lived. And it was worth the price I had to pay.[6]

Dorothy Dix

---

[6]From Carnegie, D. (1984). *How to stop worrying and start living* (pp. 252–253). New York: Simon & Schuster. Reprinted by permission.

INDEX